18

THE LOGIC OF SCIENCE

THE LOGIC OF SCIENCE

BY

HAROLD R. SMART, PH.D.

ASSISTANT PROFESSOR OF PHILOSOPHY
IN CORNELL UNIVERSITY

D. APPLETON AND COMPANY
NEW YORK LONDON
1931

PRINTED IN THE UNITED STATES OF AMERICA

PREFACE

IS mathematical knowledge the product of pure thought functioning apart from all experience? Should we say that physics is a branch of geometry; or does it tell us only of a certain orderliness amongst our purely subjective perceptions? Are substance and causality outworn conceptions, no longer applicable to natural phenomena? What possible solution can be proposed to the interminable struggle between mechanists, teleologists, and vitalists in biology? Whether evolution is a conception significant only for biological phenomena, or whether it may also be applied to wider ranges of experience, is an especially important question. Is psychology a 'natural' science? More generally, what is the aim and scope of natural science as a whole? Above all, how are we to go about answering such questions?

To be a cultured person to-day necessitates acquaintance with those wider implications of scientific ideas of which the above questions are indicative. My special interest in them resulted from the fact that mathematics and theoretical physics formed the basis of my education. It is my belief that the important influence of the natural sciences in contemporary civilization, both in their practical applications and through their remarkable theoretical advances, compels all thinking people to reflect on the significance of science for human life as a whole. For this reason the logic of science manifestly deserves a place in every college curriculum. Moreover, it should provide a common meeting ground for students specializing in science and for those whose primary interests are in logic or the other branches of philosophy.

PREFACE

It is the purpose of this book to show how these problems arose in the course of the development of the several natural sciences, to discuss solutions proposed by other writers, and finally to formulate our own conclusions about them. Only enough material has been drawn from the history of science to illustrate the argument, thus leaving it to the reader to fill in the historical record as fully as he pleases. The appended bibliography will prove helpful in this regard. Some suggestions for further study are also included, should the reader's interests incline him in that direction. The size of the book has in this way been kept down, and the exposition simplified, without, I hope, sacrificing anything essential to its main purpose.

I am indebted to Assistant Professor Stephen A. Emery of the University of North Carolina for a careful reading of the proof sheets.

H. R. S.

CONTENTS

THE LOGIC OF SCIENCE

Nor doth the eye itself,
That most pure spirit of sense, behold itself,
Not going from itself; but eye to eye opposed
Salutes each other with each other's form;
For speculation turns not to itself,
Till it hath travell'd and is mirrored there
Where it may see itself.

TROILUS AND CRESSIDA.

THE LOGIC OF SCIENCE

CHAPTER I

COMMON SENSE, SCIENCE, AND PHILOSOPHY

EVERY ONE is familiar with the conventional account of the beginnings of science among the Egyptians, the Babylonians, and the Greeks. Such practical contingencies as measuring land, making long journeys, establishing media of exchange, and so on, were responsible, it seems, for the gradual development of a rule-of-thumb knowledge of certain mathematical and physical properties and relations of things. The histories of the several sciences simply record the successive stages by which the magnificent structures of pure science have gradually built themselves up from these rude and simple foundations.

Taken by themselves, however, or even as incorporated and applied in the common-sense activities of the workaday world, specific mathematical and physical rules and formulæ by no means constitute science in the proper sense of the word. What is lacking, at this preliminary stage of man's intellectual development, is that which differentiates a full-fledged proposition of pure science from an ordinary common-sense assertion. The difference between the two may be analyzed into three factors or aspects, each of which represents, of course, a difference of degree rather than an absolute distinction.

1. First of all, common-sense knowledge is for the most part practical or pragmatic in scope and aim. But the naïvely utilitarian attitude towards knowledge, which values only its instrumental character for the attainment of the goods of life, is *ipso facto* never able to rise to an adequate apprehension of its significance as an end in itself. To grant the validity of the common pragmatic formula for the aim of science, namely prediction and control, and accordingly to accept Professor Dewey's thesis that "knowledge exists in engineering . . . more adequately than it does in . . . physics," is in principle to deny to knowledge, especially to scientific knowledge, any meaning on its own account, i.e., as a specific contribution to our understanding of 'the nature of things'—including ourselves.[1]

In reply to this observation the pragmatist may concede that no doubt knowledge as such is a 'practical good,' a satisfaction in his sense of the word, to a cer-

[1] The difference between 'natural' and 'artificial' classification nicely illustrates this point. An artificial classification is instituted merely for purposes of practical convenience, and need imply little knowledge of the subject matter of the classification. And any single, superficial attribute or quality might serve as a basis for the classification. But classification regarded as a stage of scientific knowledge becomes quite a different thing, involving the use, as its basis, of several fundamental interrelated properties of the objects to be classified. See further below, pp. 52*ff*.

tain small number of almost too ardent specialists, who cut themselves off, as far as may be, from the ordinary concerns of life in order to realize this particular good more intensely. But the drastic limitation only serves to betray more completely the essential hollowness of the concession, and places all the emphasis on the more commonplace goods within the reach of the "engineer." Accurately representing, as it does, the views of the man in the street, naïve utilitarianism would stifle that purely disinterested intellectual curiosity which is the necessary prerequisite to the attainment of wisdom, and would substitute therefor technical skill, manipulative ability, in order to make living a more comfortable business.

Tylor was right, then, when he declared that the Egyptians "knew and did not know about geometry." That is to say, they knew certain geometrical facts of practical value in measuring land, say; but they fell far short of a conception of geometry as a science exclusively devoted to the theoretical exploration of the nature of space. In short, pure science, as we to-day understand it, could not be, until man had hit upon the possibility of utilizing the bits of information so valuable from a practical point of view, as aids to his speculations about the hidden meanings of things as well. For speculation, scientific and philosophical, implies theory, and theory means a striving after unity, after unifying conceptions and principles. Where practice would rest satisfied with separate bits of information, provided the control of natural goods could thereby be secured, theory demands that the bits be woven into a pattern, that they become parts of one body of knowledge.[2]

2. A second difference or relative distinction between common sense and science concerns their respective methods of procedure, relatively to the perceptual data from which they both begin. Common sense may be said just to signify the absence of all method, unless, indeed, uncriticized assumption, crude observation, and vague conjecture deserve to go by that name. The result, of course, is dogmatic assertion, which merely reiterates itself in the face of opposition; a dogmatism embodied in miscellaneous practical rules, and impregnated with fundamental inconsistencies as between the various aspects of experience. The scientific method, on the other hand, consists of a constant criticism, within limits, of basic assumptions, methodical observations extended and supplemented wherever possible by experiment, and the formulation of hypotheses; activities which together lead to the discovery of new facts, the formulation of new laws, and the development of new, more consistent and comprehensive theories and principles of explanation.

Take for example the case of the planetary motions.

For the senses these are hopelessly irregular. . . . In the first place, since the paths of the planets are oblique to the equator, their apparent courses are spirals, not circles. In the next place Mercury and Venus at one time travel faster than the Sun, so that they get in front of it and appear as morning stars; at another time they lag behind it and appear as evening stars. In fact [to sense] these three bodies are

[2] Is it not significant, in this connection, that for the pragmatist there is no 'good,' but only 'goods'?

always "overtaking and being overtaken by one another." The other planets behave even more strangely. Sometimes they seem to accelerate their velocity so as to appear stationary among the fixed stars or even to get some way ahead of them; at other times, they are retarded and seem to have a retrograde motion. There is a further irregularity in the Sun's annual course. The solstices and equinoxes do not divide into four equal segments as we should expect them to do.[3]

The sciences of physics and astronomy gradually succeed in introducing order into this apparent chaos by formulating certain laws of motion, etc., describing the really simple and orderly as contrasted with the apparently complex and chaotic behavior of these heavenly bodies. In other words, science saves the appearances by reducing complex phenomena to relatively simple elements obeying precisely formulated laws. What previously was accepted as subject to arbitrary caprice now acquires the characteristics of dependence and necessity—marks of causal or other determination.

3. Lastly, common-sense knowledge is in one sense more concrete, in another sense more abstract, than scientific knowledge.

Common sense is more concrete in that it is closer to the objects of perception and in that science is forced to abstract from many immediately obvious aspects of objects in order to specialize on certain properties which it regards as fundamental for its particular purposes. Indeed, this necessity of specialization has even led to an apparent estrangement of science from com-

[3] Burnet, *Greek Philosophy,* Part I, "Thales to Plato," p. 346.

mon sense, and has given to scientific objects an apparent unreality as compared with the objects of more immediate sense perception. And this has caused some thinkers, like Professor Whitehead, to propose a reform in scientific methodology and conception in order to effect a reconciliation between the findings of common sense and those of science. But the reconciliation will take care of itself, if consideration is given to the complementary character of the contributions of the several sciences, instead of being restricted to one science at a time. If, for example, we compare the physicist's account of the color red with what we perceive, a marked discrepancy seems to be the only result. But if we add to what physics has to say, the findings of chemistry, the biological sciences, and psychology, the sum total of all this information, in spite of the gaps due to more or less of discontinuity between these various accounts, will actually amount to far more than what is revealed in unaided perception. And the gaps, so-called, are being closed up as science progresses, asymptotically, towards its ideal goal.

The essentially hypothetical character of scientific laws, of all scientific judgments, is another plain indication of the abstractness of science. For science there must always exist a datum, something unaccountably there, contingent (upon the balance of reality), in and by itself 'inexplicable'—to use Meyerson's word. Hence the standard form, '*if* so and so, *then* so and so,' in which the assertions of science are ultimately cast.

On the other hand, common sense is more abstract than science in that its bits of information possess no unifying bond, but tend to fly apart and even to come and go with the manifold variations of testimony, belief, and guesswork, of which the common-sense mind is composed. Once this information has been absorbed by the growing body of knowledge, however, it acquires a permanency and systematic connection which renders it relatively immune to attack by unsupported assertions from outside observers.

The greater concreteness of scientific knowledge is also brought out by the common but somewhat incoherent distinction between the subjectivity of our immediate sense impressions and the objectivity of the things of which the sense qualities are predicated. And every stage in the development of our knowledge of the external world is accompanied by an increase in this characteristic of objectivity. The significance of the theory of relativity, from this point of view, has been pointed out almost *ad nauseam;* but the same thing holds, for example, of the work of Galileo and Copernicus as compared with that of Ptolemy.

Now objectivity, in this sense of the word, means two things. It means that knowledge as it develops becomes less and less dependent (1) upon the varying and uncorroborated testimonies of individuals; and (2) upon the special conditions of time and place. By developing a technique of observation and by extending experimental laboratory control of phenomena, the scientist is able to harmonize to a greater and greater degree the confused and conflicting experiences of particular persons. What is true for one thus becomes true for all. In other words, for scientific knowledge, objectivity means *what we are obliged to think.* And in the same manner, the changes in phenomena due to differences of temporal and spatial location, or to variations in the organic conditions of our bodies, are referred, as subjective specializations, to relatively invariant relations of more or less permanent, conceptually defined objects.

We learn to measure temperature, for example, not by varying and unreliable subjective sensations, but by means of an accurately calibrated instrument which includes a scale that conveys the same message to all who read it. Or we learn to 'allow for,' i.e., to assimilate to a common measure, the variations due to special external conditions—such as the differences in the boiling point of a substance due to variations in height above sea level. In short, the constant demand for 'objectivity,' the scientific synonym for concreteness, is one of the most obvious characteristics of scientific advance. We want to know nature as she really is, not as she incoherently and ambiguously reveals herself to us through the language of the senses.

But precisely in connection with this legitimate demand there arises one very serious misconception. This misconception we must do our best to clear away, even at the risk of some digression from our main line of thought.

The point is simply this. What is objective is *ipso facto* independent of your apprehension of it, or mine. That Venus has so and so many satellites in no wise depends upon whether I or any one else has ever perceived them or not. That they are there to be discovered, and that when they are discovered, some modification of our astronomy will ensue, is, as we say, an objective fact, so far independent of our perception, volition, or mind. Such phenomena, moreover, are external to our bodies. So much is incontestable. The trouble comes in when we naïvely construe the words, 'objective' or 'independent,' and 'external,' as synonymous. Thus, the realm of objective phenomena comes to be equated merely with the so-called external world; in other words, what is properly speaking external to our bodies is erroneously regarded as in fact and principle outside of, or transcendent to, our minds. Yet, obviously, when we stop to think about it, 'external' and 'outside' and their opposites mean spatial dissociation, such as can obtain only with reference to bodies, and such as can be applied only metaphorically to the relation of mind—e.g., in the form of scientific thought—to its objects.

For the purposes of the natural scientist, happily, this misconception does not, as a usual thing, matter. Starting, as he does, from common-sense experience, he takes natural phenomena as he finds them, and proceeds to investigate their properties and relations as thoroughly as possible. He simply takes it for granted that an external world exists and is real; affording him, as such, material for investigation. And however far the natural scientist may carry his researches, he restricts himself, by hypothesis, to the study of physical phenomena. Such being the case, obviously no problem of how those phenomena ultimately may be related to our apprehension of them, can, in the usual course of affairs, arise. Thus the phrase, 'the external world,' or its equivalents, means, for the scientist, just the world in which objects, events, phenomena, are external to one another, presuppose a space-time order. And so far as the relation of our minds (rather than our bodies) to this world is concerned, perhaps the simplest assumption for all concerned would be that as time goes on these minds apprehend, learn more and more, of the nature of the physical universe of being and becoming. It follows that the problem of how minds can know the real nature of objects external to them—an 'epistemological' problem—is meaningless, because based solely on a metaphor; and that the actual question is, rather, how we can know the real nature of objects and events capable of maintaining their own independent existence.

The clue to the answer, obviously, lies in fixing the meaning of the phrase, 'independent existence.' So far as their independent existence is concerned, natural phenomena possess only physical attributes and enter into those strictly physical relationships or transactions with each other of which the laws of nature are the hypothetical formulations. There is nothing strange or profound about this, surely; nothing which in any way conflicts with common sense. And neither does the next assertion call for a great stretch of metaphysical imagination.

It is simply this: that when a natural object or phenomenon comes within our ken for the first time—when we come to know it, in other words—we have *ipso facto* succeeded in bringing it into relation with what we already know, i.e., with other objects and phenomena. After, as well as before, our apprehension of its existence, the planet Mercury no doubt continues to maintain certain relationships with other heavenly bodies, so that both its own physical existence and its relations to other things are strictly independent of our knowledge of them—a fact without which our knowledge would indeed be inexplicable. But, on the other hand, it must not be overlooked that the process of discovery, of knowledge, entails mental activity; and that hence in the very process of relating phenomena to each other in the physical world, we at the same time, in this sense, implicitly bring them into relation to a knowing subject.

Of course the two types of relationship must not be confused, for precisely such confusion gives rise to a whole breed of pseudo-epistemological problems, drives a Russell to acceptance of the ridiculous causal theory of perception, for example, and makes impossible a really logical investigation of scientific knowledge.

To determine exactly and in some detail the peculiar nature of the relation of the object to the subject in knowledge is, indeed, a formal, abstract way of stating the problem of the present work. In order not to anticipate, however, we shall now only insist that since the mind is not a thing, a physical object or container, this relationship cannot well be of the same kind as that which obtains amongst objects taken by themselves. It is neither a physical, nor a 'mental,' but a logical relationship.[4]

[4] See index for further references to this subject.

But it is high time that we return from what, for the present, is a digression, to our main theme, namely, the relation of science to common sense.

The whole matter may be summed up very simply in Huxley's thesis that science is just organized common sense. But the simplicity of the phrase must not be used to mask the tremendous significance of the development which it signalizes. Scientific achievement represents so high a level of intelligence that after two thousand five hundred years or more of effort we have not yet succeeded in assimilating it properly. Indeed, it seems that each new generation inherits automatically this ancient problem of the assimilation of science, of the harmonious adjustment of the scientific account of things with our æsthetic, moral, and religious experience. Not only that, but the rapid growth of the social sciences, so-called, and of psychology, has raised additional questions. The Germans make a distinction between the *Naturwissenschaften* and the *Geisteswissenschaften.* How important is this distinction, and what is the relation of philosophy, especially of logic, to both groups of sciences? And, finally, the matter is still further complicated by the existence, for more or less extensive periods of time, of certain pseudo-sciences, such as alchemy and astrology. For our immediate purposes, fortunately, we need consider such difficult issues as these only to the extent necessary to make clear and to justify the point of view, the procedure and aims, of the present work.

Of these questions it is convenient to begin with the one suggested last, namely, the question of differentiating between astrology and alchemy, on the one hand, and genuine science, on the other.

Astrology, if possible, deviates further from our conception of what constitutes a science than does alchemy. Alike in method, aim, and what it takes as factual data, the art of astrology fails to pursue the sure march of a science in the service of truth. The basic assumption of astrology—once widely accepted—that the stars exert their influence for the good or ill of human lives, is now thoroughly discredited. The same is necessarily true of the essentially practical aim—to predict what one's particular fate might be in virtue of the 'facts' based upon the assumption. In short, the astrologer's conception of prediction and control as the purpose of his art is wholly alien to what we understand by the spirit of scientific impartiality. As for method, nothing could well be more unscientific, for it was all a matter of following certain arbitrarily fixed rules according to which the horoscope of persons or nations was read.

The case of alchemy is somewhat different. The alchemist did at least possess certain reasonable data, but his inconsequential methods of operating upon these data involved resort to incantations and secret formulæ, and his facts were erroneously grouped together. Hence his search for the hypothetical philosopher's stone was bound to end in failure. But as soon as the general nature of the true scientific method was grasped, and new principles of classification were formulated, alchemy converted itself into chemistry, and the search for true chemical laws forthwith began.

Now these pseudo-sciences belong, no doubt, to an age that is past, and hence their only reality is a purely historical one. Nevertheless, the attitude of mind which made such intellectual monstrosities possible still persists, even in quarters where we should least expect to find it, namely, among scientists and philosophers themselves.

Does not the pragmatist, the naïve utilitarian, conceive of the aim of science in terms of the astrologer's formula of 'prediction and control'? [5] And is it not a common experience to find scientists, especially psychologists, ascribing a potency to certain theoretical constructs to control and explain spiritual realities, just as the astrologer worshiped and feared the stars because of their similar power? Think of the resourcefulness of the 'complex' idea to explain the creations of artistic genius, or of the skill of the behaviorist in reducing thought to a physical event, or of the psychological explanation (or explaining away) of philosophical theories! The sober conservatives among scientists usually describe such conceptions as more or less 'metaphysical,' thereby intending to condemn them as thoroughly as possible. But perhaps it would be more appropriate, and historically more accurate, to regard them as the vestigial remains of the 'black arts,' carried over into an age that is properly described as primarily scientific. We should note in passing, how-

[5] Of course science does predict, both backwards and forwards, but primarily for the purposes of advancing knowledge as such, rather than for the practical control of events or things. Is it more than a mere coincidence that both astrology and pragmatism should construe science as an art?

ever, that the curiously persistent demand for a set of rules to make easy the thorny path of knowledge is only another manifestation of the same intellectual idiosyncrasies. Bacon, Descartes, John Stuart Mill—with his famous 'methods'—and the mathematical logicians of all times have ardently pursued this methodological will-o'-the-wisp.[6]

Unfortunately the task of distinguishing genuine science from pseudo-science is not the greatest difficulty which thinkers have had to face in the process of acquiring a clear understanding of the ultimate significance and value of scientific knowledge. A far greater difficulty is that of determining the relation of science to philosophy, and, since logic is a part of philosophy, of more specifically determining the subject of the present work.

It is common knowledge that for the earliest Greek philosophers there existed no distinction between science and philosophy; on the contrary, asking only one question, they sought only one answer. Other questions, however, were not slow in arising, and accordingly, in order to effect a synthesis, embracing all aspects of experience, Plato had first of all to distinguish sharply between them. His conception of the various levels of intelligence, conveyed by the figure of the divided line, stands to-day as a bold outline, indicating one possible method of assimilating scientific knowledge to other

[6] See below, p. 98. An analogous demand often appears in the sphere of ethics. According to some thinkers, ethics should furnish us with a set of rules to guide our conduct under any given circumstances. How easy life would thus become—and how stupidly inhuman!

knowledge and to art, religion, and so on, without destroying any of them. Aristotle had to face the same issues and likewise contributed much to their solution, both by practically inaugurating several of the special sciences, and by his foundation of the science of logic and a metaphysics of the categories. Indeed, so astoundingly fruitful were the endeavors of these thinkers that scholars still find not only the spirit but much of the detail of their philosophizing informing and significant.

But with the increasing pressure of political, social, and especially of religious interests, the interest in pure science proportionately declined, not to flourish again until the Renaissance and later. And obviously no problem with regard to the nature, aim, and methods of science can arise so long as science does not exist or occupy an important place among intellectual pursuits. On the other hand, the history of the several sciences from the Renaissance to the present day is little more than the account of one astounding development after another. Not only that, but through its practical applications to problems arising in other spheres, science exercises a tremendous influence and fascination over minds quite incapable of grasping its true significance and limitations. So that for long it has been, is now, and undoubtedly will indefinitely continue to be one of the most absorbing of human activities and interests.

From the point of view of the student of the logic of science this state of affairs has both its advantages and its disadvantages. The advantages consist precisely in the abundance of the material of scientific advance with which the history of modern science supplies us. Students of to-day are, in this respect, as compared with Plato and Aristotle and even the philosophers of the early modern period, in a most fortunate position. On the other hand, progress in science has been so rapid and its revelations so revolutionizing and startling that an impartial evaluation of its ultimate significance still remains a desideratum rather than an achievement. The unconventional fashion in which science has time and again overturned and uprooted the various 'idols' with which, as Bacon taught, mankind is beset, has made for science enemies swayed by prejudice, as well as friends grown over-enthusiastic and blind to any possible limitations of the scientific point of view. To say, for example, that this is a scientific age and that philosophy had best be scientific too, if it cherishes its own preservation, while possibly justified as a true expression of the intellectual temper of the time, may appear upon examination as excessive as the complementary absurdity of the religious fanatic who calls all scientists fools and atheists. Perhaps thinkers of a later, more disillusioned age will compare our naïvely optimistic belief that philosophy, by becoming scientific, is bound to make progress in the definitive solution of its fundamental problems, to a hitherto unknown extent, with the cheerful optimism of a Bacon, looking forward to the theoretical and practical conquest of all nature in a few decades. Is there not the same blindness to possible limitations and difficulties in the one case as in the other?

This matter is important enough to warrant some particular consideration in the present context. We may well ask ourselves precisely what is meant by those who propose to identify in some fashion or other the two fields of inquiry: science and philosophy. Our answers to this question will at least instruct us as to what the phrase defining logic as 'the science of the sciences' does not mean; with the ground thus cleared we may then go on to find out what, properly speaking, the definition actually does mean.

Certain thinkers of the New-Realism school, for example, urge the application to philosophical problems of the scientific method, so-called. Without stopping to ask whether there are any important differences of subject matter and problems which might be of significance in this respect, these philosophers argue directly from the patent success of the scientific method in dealing with external phenomena, to its promise of success when applied to ultimate philosophical issues.[7] But it would seem that a fatal objection to this doctrine lies in the fact that prior to its use in philosophy the method to be employed must *ex hypothesi* have been independently formulated. And to accomplish this task *ipso facto* necessitates going beyond the method itself to something more fundamental. In other words, clearly, the problem of the formulation of the method is quite distinct from the matter of its application. A vicious circle would necessarily result from any attempt

[7] One could, of course, very well raise the question whether the New-Realist conception of what constitutes scientific method were correct or not; but for our immediate purposes we do not need to raise this particular issue.

to apply a given scientific method to its own formulation. It follows, therefore, that there is at least one ultimate philosophical problem to which the scientific method as such does not and cannot apply. And this inescapable fact is certainly enough to raise the gravest doubts about the whole point of view behind such a procedure. Conversely—as we shall see more fully presently—the logic of science must be something more than, though it may well include, a description of scientific methodology.

Instead of the method, then, we may claim for the content of some science or group of sciences a peculiar significance in the sphere of philosophy. For example, one readily calls to mind the use, or abuse, of evolution in this regard. To take evolution seriously in philosophy means to think of man as a part of the natural order, i.e., simply as a biological organism. Like all other living things, man is engaged, on this view, in a struggle with his environment, in the course of which he has developed a tool, the intellect, for the mutual adjustment of organism and environment. Also science is an art, the product of the efficient functioning of the intellect, while the business of logic is to bring to consciousness the technique of rules otherwise blindly and haphazardly applied to the attainment of the practical ends of life. In short, life, on this view, is the highest philosophical category, while the human mind becomes an instrument, a function, for the promotion of life.[8] Unquestionably this form of 'instru-

[8] As has often been pointed out, the question how such a philosophical theory as this happened to arise, if its fundamental as-

mentalism,' as it might be called, is exceedingly flattering to one branch of science, and it may well serve on that account as an additional inspiration to research. Then, too, other sciences, for example the social sciences, so-called, gain a ready-made set of technical terms and even a complete literary vocabulary, in exchange for their adoption of the 'evolutionary point of view.' In short, both sides to this intellectual transaction seem at first sight to have made a good bargain.

Too bad that competition always hovers in the immediate background, eager to wrest at least part of the 'unearned increment' from its too confident possessors! That is to say, a speculatively inclined physicist, like Ostwald, has no difficulty or compunction about proposing, as a counterpart to 'evolutionism,' a doctrine, say, of 'energism.' And similarly the Driesches and the Croces quickly come forward with their philosophies of 'vitalism' and of 'historicism.' And in the end, perhaps, the resulting competition may, if unchecked, lead to intellectual bankruptcy.

For it becomes quickly evident to the disinterested logician that where the same fundamental assumption leads, in different hands, to such divergent results, there objective truth is not to be had, on any terms. The proof is in principle as easy, for example, and consequently as unconvincing, that mind, or thought, is a function of energy, as that it is a function of life, and that it is a function of a depersonalized historical proc-

sumptions are true, seems to the hostile critic very hard to answer. In other words, just what is the pragmatic value of instrumentalism itself?

ess, as of either. Consequently the end result can only be a *reductio ad absurdum* of this whole line of reasoning. What alone is philosophical in these various tendencies is simply the fact that they provide a striking illustration of man's natural inclination to speculate, on whatever basis his training and experience may afford him, concerning the more ultimate problems of human experience and human destiny.

Another very widespread and attractive—but nevertheless erroneous—view regarding the relation of science to philosophy finds expression in the doctrine that the principal difference between the two inquiries resides in the fact that the latter is more comprehensive than the former. The sciences, it is said, formulate laws relating to the various special fields of investigation. Logic, or philosophy, on the other hand, formulates laws of universal applicability, whatever be the content of our thought. In other words, logic would appear to be merely an extension of science in the ordinary sense of the word; and since on this view logic is of the very essence of philosophy, we may say shortly that philosophy is simply scientific generalization carried to its utmost limit of abstractness. Thus, according to Russell, "starting with premises which . . . belong to logic, and arriving at results which as obviously belong to mathematics, we find that there is no point at which a sharp line can be drawn with logic to the left and mathematics to the right." [9] Or, according to S.

[9] Russell, *Introduction to Mathematical Philosophy,* p. 94. Cf. also the present writer's *The Philosophical Presuppositions of Mathematical Logic,* Chap. IV.

Alexander, "the more comprehensive a science becomes, the closer it comes to philosophy, so that it may be difficult to say where the science leaves off and philosophy begins." [10]

Now a little reflection will reveal the complete impossibility of maintaining such a facile doctrine as this. It tacitly presupposes (as critics of Alexander's view have naturally observed) that a science like biology, say, deals with phenomena which at bottom are reducible without remainder to processes of inanimate matter; and the latter, in the end, to the mathematical relations of space, time and number. On the contrary, as Meyerson's well-known works, *Identité et réalité* and *De l'explication dans les sciences*, abundantly prove, there is a specificity in phenomena, something fundamental in the nature of things, which it is hopeless to anticipate will one day or in principle find expression without remainder in mathematical equations or the *a priori* formulæ of formal logic.

It is true, of course, that philosophy is more comprehensive than any science or group of sciences, but what these thinkers seem for the moment to forget is that there are other equally important distinctions, of a qualitative nature, between the two subjects. But the confusion, unfortunately, does not limit itself to this point. For while there are many who are willing to concede a qualitative difference, as well as greater comprehensiveness, to the problems of philosophy, they nevertheless argue, with Professor Montague,[11] that the

[10] Alexander, *Space, Time and Deity,* Vol. I, p. 2.
[11] Cf. *The Social Sciences,* p. 467.

sciences are constantly encroaching on ground that formerly belonged to philosophy, so that by implication the subject matter of the latter is what is left over to conjecture and vague, unfounded speculation, when science, with its precision and clarity, has gone as far as possible. There is a very widespread feeling among scientists, especially, that this is a correct statement of the case; that, qualitatively regarded, the formulations of philosophy are vague, uncertain, and unverifiable, as compared with those of the natural sciences.

Among all the errors which these untenable views contain, there exists, at least implicitly, one important truth. Namely, there is a demand for unity and concreteness in what is true and real. But there is serious misunderstanding as to how to realize these conditions of genuine insight. Concrete unity must include differences, not exclude them; and philosophy is not only more comprehensive in scope and interest than is science, but its problems are very certainly in no inconsiderable part the outcome, not the vestigial remains, of scientific advance. It seems evident, therefore, that philosophy cannot be impoverished but must rather be enriched by progress in other domains; in other words, the growth of knowledge or insight is a real development which involves not alone a greater comprehensiveness but also a greater concreteness, in the field of philosophy as elsewhere.

What this means, specifically, we shall try to explain more fully presently. In the meantime we must note in passing one other serious misconception with regard to the relation of science to philosophy.

Just as there is a tendency, fallacious in principle, to import the methods and problems of science into philosophy, so there is a counter fallacy of construing the task of logic as that of devising a technique, a set of rules, for the manipulation of the objects of inquiry. Both practically and theoretically such a problem proves, upon examination, incapable of solution. Not only are the technical procedures of the various sciences infinitely various; but new ones are constantly being devised when and as the demand arises. How easy it is to enumerate the shortcomings of a Bacon or a Descartes from this point of view! And although writers of elementary textbooks on logic still give considerable space to an exposition of Mill's 'methods' of scientific induction, the scientist has rarely troubled himself with the question as to whether or not he was actually following any such set of rules. The hard truth of the matter is that scientific research, like moral conduct, is a sphere where the particular human being must learn to shift for himself; if for no other reason, then because the spirit of free untrammeled inquiry, so characteristic of science at its best, will tolerate no artificial restrictions from without, but will always be guided, in principle, by what the subject matter itself demands.[12]

So much for what the phrase, 'science of the sciences,' as applied to logic does not mean; now it is high time to make good our promise to explain what positively it does mean.

[12] Cf. the present writer's article, in *The Journal of Philosophy*, Vol. XXIII, No. 4 (Feb., 1926), pp. 85*ff*., entitled "Prolegomena to the Logic of Science."

And here is the place to recall what was said a little above to the effect that in all knowledge a relation of subject to object at least implicitly obtains. According to that idea, natural science investigates the structure and the processes of 'external' phenomena, i.e., of phenomena or events conceived of as comprising an existential realm of being, spatio-temporally determined, and by hypothesis independent of our apprehension of it. A botanist, for example, devotes all his energies to an exploration of the affinities and evolution of plants, and he applies the principles of biology in an effort to understand their history. In the course of his investigations he observes, classifies, experiments, theorizes, describes, and explains, seeking to the best of his ability to render intelligible the region of concrete fact that he finds as a datum before him. Thus the scientist, *qua* scientist, has no other concern than what is strictly involved in his attempt to decipher the order of nature.

But not only does the plant world—to keep to our example—possess a structure and an organization; by a kind of automatic reflection the science of botany itself (and the other natural sciences), conceived of now as part of the general body of knowledge, at the same time endows its content with a form or systematic organization. Hence, in turn, the logical problem naturally arises as to just how classification, explanation, observation, experiment, theory, themselves regarded as given phenomena, exemplify the general forms and methods of knowledge. As Joseph so admirably expresses it,

What "the courses of the stars" are to astronomy, what figures, lines, and surfaces are to geometry, what plants are to botany, . . . that the other sciences are to the logician: they are the material which he has to investigate, the particular facts which are given him, in order that he may discover the principles displayed in them. He has to ask what knowledge is as knowledge, . . . and he must therefore examine divers "knowledges" and see in what they are alike; and among the best pieces of knowledge that exist, the best "knowledges," are the various sciences. But he is not concerned with the detail of any particular science, but only with those *kinds* (or forms) of thinking which are exemplified in all our thinking—though not necessarily the same in all—but best exemplified in the sciences.[13]

If we may define zoölogy, say, as a science or connected discourse about living things, then, analogously, logic may be described as the science which treats of the general characteristics of connected discourse. It is a discourse about discourse.

In sum, then, knowledge, regarded from the point of view of the object known, endows that object, as quasi-given, factual matter, with form; and knowledge, regarded from the point of view of the subject knowing (i.e., the human intellect), itself comprises a content organized according to what we may appropriately call the forms of the scientific intelligence or the scientific mind.

But if this be a necessary and legitimate way in which to view the relation of logic—more generally, philosophy—to science, then our contention (above) that philosophy gains rather than loses in content as science advances, needs no further proof. And the advance

[13] Joseph, *An Introduction to Logic,* 2nd ed., pp. 3, 4.

in logic since the days of Bacon, closely paralleling the development in the sciences, abundantly testifies to the truth of this view.

It is the scientific intelligence, then, understood in this sense of the word, which furnishes the material and the problems of the logic of science.

The principal source of this material is, of course, the historical record of the several sciences. Herein lies, indeed, the greatest general significance of the history of science—to minister in this way to an ever clearer understanding of the structure and process of scientific inference. Compared with this, the mere narrative account of the successive stages of scientific investigation, including dates, names, and specific individual accomplishments—which is all that the usual history of science amounts to—is of slight importance. It is right enough, no doubt, to regard a knowledge of the accomplishments of the great scientists as an essential part of one's education. But, except for the specialist, there is little more of cultural significance in this department of history. The use of these records in the fashion indicated above, on the other hand, while seldom adopted, is the one possible method of transmuting scientific knowledge into wisdom.

On this view the logic of science teaches us no new facts; its function being rather to put the facts we already know in a new light; and in this new light they may be said to reveal the nature of mind, so far as it is scientific, whereas they originally taught us something about the nature of the external world. Hence until scientific knowledge has been interpreted in this way it cannot be said to have been philosophized, made a genuine part of our spiritual culture.

These facts, the findings of science, 'are made to reveal the nature of mind, so far as it is scientific'—what precisely does this assertion mean? To answer this question is, as we have seen, the real problem of the logic of science, and consequently only the general nature of the answer can be indicated here, and that again only in an abstract, preliminary fashion.

Mathematics, the physical sciences, biology and psychology, together make up the domain of natural science; and together they yield us the most substantial part, certainly, of our knowledge of the external world. We shall be occupied, accordingly, in what follows, with the structural development of these sciences. This means that we have to ask what are the fundamental assumptions of the several sciences, what are their specific aims, what is the general nature of the reasoning processes involved in each case, and whether there are any peculiarities of subject matter worthy of note from the logical point of view.

For example, thinkers have argued, pro and con, that substance and causality are the two fundamental conceptions—categories—of physical science, and that inference in this domain consequently depends upon the assumption of the principle of the uniformity of nature. Other questions, of a similar nature, concern the relation of mathematics to the natural sciences, the precise meaning of evolution as contrasted with other processes of change, and the determination of the categories appropriate to the study of living things.

A more striking illustration of the kind of special problems which will concern us in what follows is to be found in mathematics. Many mathematicians and logicians have held that mathematics is a purely formal, deductive science, the product of pure thought functioning independently of all experience. This view, however, manifestly involves so many questionable assumptions that it is the logician's duty to investigate it very carefully. First of all, it involves a fundamental dichotomy between reason and experience, a dichotomy otherwise theoretically useless as well as very difficult to justify. It presupposes, further, that deduction and induction are independent processes of inference, whereas so far as every other science is concerned deduction and induction seem rather to be fundamentally related to each other as complementary aspects of a single process. And it of course makes mathematics unique among the sciences as being devoid of all experiential content.

So much by way of indicating the nature of the problems to be dealt with in the present work. Perhaps a word needs to be added in order to make clear just how the solution of such problems as these may enable us to throw light not only on the nature of mind, but on certain other philosophical problems as well.

For this purpose the conflict between contingency and absolute determinism readily offers itself. Many philosophers [14] have argued that the growing evidence

[14] Of whom Boutroux may serve as a leading representative. Cf. his *Contingency in the Laws of Nature*. And see the discussion between Professor Sheldon and the present writer in *The Philo-*

of contingency, and the apparent breakdown of absolute determinism, in the sphere of natural phenomena, afforded proof of at least a certain amount of free choice in the sphere of human conduct. Now what the student of the logic of science may here point out is the essential opposition between the two conceptions—contingency and freedom. The correlative of the former is determinism; of the latter, slavery, subservience to an end and purpose formulated by others for their own exclusive benefit. So far as nature is concerned, surely, man is neither free nor unfree; it is only in relation to his fellows that he enjoys freedom or suffers domination from without. Thus it is clear that the logician of science has to do only with the antithesis between contingency and determinism and not at all with that between freedom and its opposite.

Or again, with regard to mathematical reasoning: The view commonly held that mathematics is a wholly formal, deductive science obviously implies certain definite ideas as to the nature of mind, *qua* scientific, such as its division into clear-cut faculties (e.g., reason, sensation, intuition), and correspondingly separate processes. But the faculty psychology is now in professional disrepute, and while there might be some difficulty in defining what has taken its place, it seems at all events clear that no logician ought to compromise himself by trying to bolster up such an outworn creed solely for certain 'metaphysical' reasons of his own.

In concluding this discussion of the relation of phi-

sophical Review, Vol. XXXII, p. 335, and Vol. XXXIII, pp. 73 and 286.

losophy—more especially logic—to science two points call for special consideration. These points are (1) the relation of the logic of natural science to logic in general; and (2) the significance, for our purposes, of the most recent advances in the several sciences.

1. The first point has already to some extent been dealt with, at least by implication, in the preceding pages. But on so important a matter repetition is surely excusable, if not, indeed, essential. Logic, in general, we may say, assumes the existence of a developing body of knowledge, as a secure possession of man, and as in principle revealing the actual nature of the real world. The work of logic is accordingly to analyze this knowledge, with a view to determining its structure and process of development. And, since judgment or inference is the intellectual activity by which knowledge comes to be, we may say with Bradley that the direct and primary purpose of logic, in general, is "to set out the general essence and the main types of inference and judgment, and, with regard to each of these, to explain its nature and special merits and defects."[15] From this point of view the problem of the logic of science will be to determine "the main types of inference and judgment" which come to be in the several sciences, and thus to make that part of the sum total of human knowledge aware of its own nature and presuppositions. This statement, taken in conjunction with what has been said before, ought to make sufficiently clear the aim and method of the present work. Obviously there exist similar problems with re-

[15] Bradley, *The Principles of Logic,* 2nd ed., p. 620.

gard to other departments of knowledge, e.g., history in all its forms and subdivisions—but those must be the concern of another time.

2. It is easy to see that from our point of view the philosophical significance of the most recent advances in the several sciences will generally be much less than is often maintained from other points of view. For it is not with the specific detailed content of a science that we are primarily or mainly concerned, but rather with those comparatively abiding features of the content and form which survive a transient expression in the 'current literature' on the subject. And any particular scientific fact—such, e.g., as the melting point of some chemical substance—has probably less interest for us than has the existence of any ordinary daisy for the botanist. A writer like Russell, on the other hand, seems obliged to modify many of the details of his philosophy to keep pace with each new scientific advance, such as the quantum theory. In fact the whole philosophy of events may not unfairly be regarded as an effort to construct a world-view in keeping with, if not directly based upon, the latest important developments in physical science. But since our problem is different, so also is our attitude towards these and other such developments. What we have to ask regarding them by its very nature cannot be answered satisfactorily, or in more than highly tentative fashion, until they have been thoroughly digested by the sciences in question. And just as we regard those scientists as mistaken who tried to decide between various types of geometry by a test which could not

but validate one of them—namely, the one implicitly presupposed by the very nature of the test—so we must regard those philosophers as ill-advised who seek to validate a system of philosophy mainly by its congruence with some contemporary scientific development, seeing that the philosophical theory not infrequently has been propounded *a priori* precisely to that end. And, as we have previously argued, the mere reformulation and generalization of scientific ideas, unsupported by other, more ultimate considerations, cannot in themselves supply an answer to ultimate philosophical questions.

Our primary objectives in this chapter have been three in number. (1) We have tried clearly to distinguish scientific knowledge from common sense. (2) We have discussed rather briefly certain misconceptions of the relation of science to philosophy. (3) And we have endeavored to define, clearly and precisely, the problem of the present work. Certain minor points also have come up for necessarily rather summary treatment; such, for instance, as the difference between the pseudo-sciences and genuine science, and the so-called epistemological problem of how minds 'inside' our heads can know objects assumed to exist independently 'outside' our heads. In the next chapter we shall find ourselves occupied with certain further preliminary issues which must be cleared out of the way before we can proceed, in a straightforward and unambiguous manner, to grapple with more specific problems.

CHAPTER II

THE GENERAL PRESUPPOSITIONS, METHODS, AND AIMS OF NATURAL KNOWLEDGE

THERE are three general problems which we must undertake to solve if we are to grasp the real meaning of scientific inference. (1) We must make explicit the presuppositions which underlie natural knowledge; (2) we must define what is meant by 'the scientific method'; and (3) we must formulate a clear idea of the aim or aims of scientific inquiry.

1. On the first of these problems we have already had something to say in the preceding chapter.[1] For natural science, to paraphrase a famous saying of Hegel's, the real is the existential and the existential is the real. Things, material objects, their perceptual properties, their mutual relations, the observable processes or changes which they undergo and in which they participate—such are the obvious realities of this domain. Set in a spatio-temporal framework, they are, as the current phraseology has it, 'independent of our knowledge of them,' though of course in principle knowable, and 'externally' conditioned by one another. Simply by keeping in mind these basic limitations of subject matter, and the methodological point of view from which it is regarded, we may hope for a reasonable degree of success in our subsequent attempts to define

[1] P. 9.

the content of the several natural sciences in particular. That from the point of view of the ultimate principles of reality, such a universe of discourse is essentially a part only, a fragment, of the concrete totality of experience, is, of course, obvious. And when we come to discuss our third question as to the aims of scientific knowledge, we shall have to bear these presuppositions and limitations clearly in mind.

2. Our second main objective is to obtain some insight into the general nature of scientific methodology. It is important to remember here the distinction alluded to in the preceding chapter, between problems of technique and problems of method. With the former logicians have practically no concern, while for scientists the latter are, generally speaking, of as little interest.

The two universally recognized moments of the process of scientific inference are deduction and induction. Some thinkers, it is true, would regard this statement as erroneous, or at least misleading. For it seems to imply that these moments are equally important, and that any complete bit of reasoning involves both. That mathematics is a purely deductive science is a glib and ready characterization which apparently contradicts the validity of this thesis. But in the following chapters we shall have to oppose this rather widely prevalent view, as well as the correlative doctrine that 'pure mathematics' and 'logic' are to all intents and purposes inseparable. With regard to sciences like physics and biology, on the other hand, no one disputes a place to induction; the only question is, what precisely is its rôle. Authorities—and these not the extreme rationalists and *apriorists* alone—could be cited for the view that induction is only a preparatory stage in any complete process of inference. And, on the other hand, many empiricists would incline to the Baconian philosophy in this matter. Here again, as in so many other cases, a study of conflicting authorities very successfully demonstrates the necessity of an independent analysis of the process of scientific inference, with a view to a more precise and careful determination of what we can legitimately mean by induction and what by deduction.

For to accept the customary account of what induction and deduction are, inevitably leads to conflict, to a preferential bias in one direction or the other. The empiricist, with his predilection for facts, or sense phenomena, naturally regards induction as starting from them, and he can see in the result of the process nothing more than a summary statement concerning a multitude, an aggregate of such phenomena. That *A*, *B*, *C*, . . . are bodies that gravitate are particular facts. That all bodies gravitate is the summary general statement, the 'law,' derived from the appropriate observations and experiments. The rationalist, with his equally sincere bias for generalization, endeavors to formulate *a priori* the most comprehensive formal logical propositions or postulates possible, in order subsequently to 'deduce' therefrom—more accurately, to subsume thereunder—not only the facts of this world, but all possible particularizations of all possible worlds.

Now the striking fact about these doctrines is, that they both assume as fundamental in all reasoning the principle of class inclusion or the abstract universal.[2] However much they may differ on other points, both rationalists and empiricists adopt what has been aptly called the 'linear' conception of inference.[3]

On this view the problem of the inductive method, so-called, is to show how from propositions, which represent immediately valid judgments about certain particular experiences, we may arrive at propositions valid of the entire class of such experiences. What guarantees the validity of a general law covering all instances, if one starts from a particular statement true of a few instances; that is, is such a general statement absolutely certified, or is it only the expression of probability? Many of us in our school days learned to look upon induction as this process of inference from particulars to particulars, its test being prediction (not explanation), and its method being association of images or unanalyzed likenesses by contiguity in coexistence or succession.

The process and problem of deduction is of course regarded as just the inverse of this. What are the few absolutely valid general propositions, from which we can deduce all the special laws and particular propositions of ordinary experience? Unlike induction, which, as above conceived, can of course yield only probable results, deduction is popularly supposed to yield absolutely certain conclusions.

[2] This unfortunate phrase, though justified by usage, is misleading. It does *not* mean what it seems to imply, that there really are various kinds of universals—'abstract,' 'concrete'—and does mean, if anything, the universal, regarded or conceived as an abstract common name, a least common denominator of its particulars.

[3] Cf. Bosanquet, *Implication and Linear Inference.*

Such, then, are the general problems of scientific method, as conceived by exponents of the linear inference point of view. As for their solution, that is to be achieved by the formulation of certain rules of procedure. The logician is to provide these rules and the scientist is to apply them. This division of labor is merely arbitrary or pragmatic, however, for between logic and science—on this view—in its more general aspects there exists no real line of division. In this fashion did Bacon and Descartes and certain descendants of theirs conceive of the problem of scientific method—at least if we are to believe the common interpretations of their philosophies.[4] The present-day inheritors of this family tradition are scattered about in every land, and obviously he must be bold who presumes to question it. Yet question it by plain implication we already have, and we must now endeavor to defend ourselves.

In plain language, this conception of inference as linear is as superficial and inadequate—and in any case as impossible of realization—as it is widespread. Granted that, as the result of an inductive process, our range of intellectual vision is indeed enlarged, quantitatively extended, what exponents of the doctrine of linear inference forget is that it is also modified in other and possibly more important respects. And granted that *if* the premises are true, and *if* the reasoning is correctly performed, the conclusion of a deduc-

[4] On Descartes cf. however R. M. Blake, "The Rôle of Experience in Descartes' Theory of Method," *The Philosophical Review,* Vol. XXXVIII, Nos. 2 and 3, pp. 125*ff.*, 201*ff.*

tive process is also bound to be true, what is forgotten is precisely these important provisos. As soon as we attempt to fill in the blank forms of the syllogism or of any other type of demonstration, we find that in principle one or more elements of uncertainty always accompany our efforts. The frequent acknowledgment that the conclusion of a line of reasoning is really more certain than the premises on which it is based is but a naïve confirmation of this state of affairs. Neither is there any possibility of realizing the goal set for induction according to the linear conception. For as soon as we succeed in including all instances within the scope of our formula, thus achieving certainty in that respect, the induction ceases to be such; we have instead a mere enumeration of particulars, which, as Bacon long ago pointed out, "is a puerile thing," not really an inference at all.

When, on the other hand, we examine for ourselves any complete bit of scientific reasoning, beginning with the facts and initial considerations which instigated the subsequent investigation, proceeding to the formulation of an hypothesis, and concluding with its verification—or modification, or rejection—together with all the intermediate stages, partial failures, new beginnings, and the new, but still imperfect, insight into a whole range of phenomena, we see how far short of adequacy, of a faithful representation of reality, these linear schemes and schedules really are.[5]

[5] This, no doubt, is one reason why the usual textbook presentation of scientific truth seems so artificial and stilted. The textbook too often consists of a series of formal demonstrations, the

An anatomist, for example, may have examined separately various organs, tubes, liquids, etc., in the several parts of the human body, without ever having hit upon the theory of the circulation of the blood. As a matter of fact, historians tell us that Harvey 'proved' eight points in his treatise on the circulation of the blood. Which of these points he established by direct observation and which by inference we do not know. So far as we can see, all of them, severally, might have been established either way, though plainly not all, collectively, could be established by abstract reasoning alone.

But it happens that one of them, though subsequently corroborated by observation, was reached by Harvey . . . through inference alone. This point was the fundamental one—by itself almost a theory of the circulation—that the blood in the arteries and the veins is the same blood; that is to say, that it, or most of it, runs through from the arteries into the veins, instead of belonging, as had previously been supposed, to separate systems by which different kinds of blood were circulated through the veins and arteries from the right and left ventricles respectively. Harvey himself never saw the "capillary channels" by which the blood actually passes from the arteries to the veins.

Other essential points, in correction of previous opinion, were that the heart by its muscular contraction was the motor power of the circulation; that there was no passage for blood through the division between the chambers of the heart, so that the whole of the blood passes from the right to the left ventricle through the lungs and not through the interior of

dried husks of research, omitting much of the detail, and to a considerable extent covering up the obscurities and the always tentative nature of the results under a semblance of vigorous, flawless proof. Hence is engendered an entirely erroneous conception of the actual state of affairs.

the heart; and by combining this point with that above mentioned as in the first instance inferred, that the whole of the blood in the left ventricle is driven by it through the arteries of the body into the veins, by which it returns to the heart.

It is the logical interest of this investigation . . . that it looks, *prima facie,* as if the investigator had really nothing to do but to observe and set down each of the eight points (which nevertheless . . . he "proves") in order to demonstrate the whole character of the complex, that is, to discern the "circulation" of the blood.[6]

Such direct observation as had been made in the previous history of science had failed to establish anything approaching to the system in its true character, however, while as a result of Harvey's bold inference these particular observable data themselves acquired a new quality as elements in a systematic complex.

Here, then, is a new body of truth, gained by a procedure which is unquestionably at once both inductive and deductive. Our knowledge has been extended quantitatively and improved qualitatively at one and the same time.

And this example, so far from being exceptional, is a truly typical exemplification of the scientific method in general. Newton's laws were no mere generalizations of the laws of Kepler and Galileo; as everybody knows, they also gave an entirely new meaning to the work of the earlier men. Even in mathematics we find that the same thing obtains. There is no more evidence in mathematics than in any other science, to corroborate the linear-inference doctrine. In no science, in no complete piece of reasoning, do we, as a matter of fact, pass

[6] Bosanquet, *op. cit.,* pp. 75 *ff.*

directly along a graduated scale from generals to particulars, or *vice versa,* without the aid of something which corresponds to the middle term of the syllogism. Thus we can deduce from a general mathematical formula, such as that for a curve of the second order, the special geometrical forms of the circle, ellipse, etc., "only by considering a certain parameter which occurs in them and by permitting it to vary through a continuous series of magnitudes." And conversely, "the new forms of negative, irrational and transfinite numbers are not added to the number-system from without, but grow out of the continuous unfolding of the fundamental logical function that was effective in the first beginnings of the system." [7]

The use of the word "system," in this connection, is significant. For it means a number of facts, which as bound together in the system we may call elements, possessing both mutual relations, of which a law, theorem, or formula is the expression, and individual characteristics, not inferable from the law or formula alone. Hence, in order to infer deductively the individual characteristics of some of the elements, we must know, in addition to their mutual relations to all of the others, the individual characteristics of some of the others. Conversely, in order to infer inductively an hypothesis or law from certain facts at first taken separately, we must not merely know their individual characteristics, but we must seek to verify (by observation, experiment, analogical reasoning, etc.) the assumption that there obtains some identity of nature, some systematic or-

[7] Cassirer, *Substance and Function,* pp. 20, 67.

ganization underlying or pervading them, and so relating them to each other.

An analysis of these examples gives us a more profound and inclusive, if also a more difficult, idea of the general nature of scientific inference. It is more inclusive, because it can account adequately for processes of reasoning which on the linear doctrine must remain an insoluble problem.[8] It is more profound in that it looks upon induction and deduction, not as two separate methods or techniques, but as two inseparable aspects of that process of reasoning which has as its main task the progressive deepening and extending of the knowledge we already possess. Indeed, we claim as a virtue distinctive of this conception that it is the only one which enables us to render a true evaluation of the results of any bit of reasoning. On the linear view, as we have seen, deduction yields absolutely true propositions, while a greater or less degree of probability is all that we can hope to obtain from the so-called inverse process of induction. Thence arises the intolerably vexatious and perennial 'problem of induction': how, *per impossibile*, to attain inductive generalizations as rigorously valid and true as the propositions arrived at by a deductive procedure are supposed to be. As a matter of fact, and as our doctrine directly implies, however, scientific truth is never either absolute or merely probable, in the linear-inference sense of those words. Actually, a 'true' scientific proposition is one which, so far as our present knowledge extends, holds

[8] Cf. "The Problem of Induction," by the present writer, in the *Journal of Philosophy,* Vol. XXV, No. 1, pp. 18*ff*.

absolutely, but one which we nevertheless recognize as subject to correction or qualification in the light of the new developments—new facts discovered, new theories formulated—that in the course of time are bound to ensue. Even though certain verbal and symbolical formulæ may retain their places in the developing body of knowledge which is science, their meaning undergoes a no less certain alteration from age to age. The relativity theory in physics, the rise of non-Euclidean geometry and the alterations of the number-system in mathematics, no less than Darwin's contributions to the biological sciences, exemplify this state of affairs.

There are a host of other, minor points connected with the methodology of science, which we have not yet touched upon. The use and abuse of analogy, for instance, is an interesting subject, and others are the rôle of observation and experiment, the formulation and function of hypotheses, the process of verification, the combination of analysis and synthesis, and so on. But since all of these points receive a great deal of competent attention from the writers of the current textbooks on logic, and since no important controversial issues arise in connection with them, it seems hardly necessary to treat of them here.[9]

In concluding this part of our study we should, however, refer briefly to another permissible meaning of the phrase, 'the scientific method,' as applied to *any* object or objects of inquiry. To be scientific, in this, the wider sense of the word, is simply to proceed in an

[9] These and similar points are also well handled by Wolf, *Essentials of Scientific Method.*

orderly manner, and in the light of some clear guiding principles, with the investigation of a given subject matter. Precisely what the order, what the guiding principles are to consist in, is of course for those competent in any given field to decide. The German word, *Wissenschaft*, accurately conveys this meaning, and accordingly is applied indifferently to history, to mathematics, to philosophy, to economics, to geography, and so on. One advantage of retaining this wider usage is that it serves, or ought to serve, to disabuse our minds of the prejudice—very rampant in some quarters and among some philosophers even—in favor of the natural sciences, as in some favored, exclusive sense, yielding knowledge of a more significant, more real kind than can be obtained anywhere else or in any other way. The truth of the matter is, of course, that, with respect to its particular subject matter, natural science rightly claims this superiority; but it goes without saying that the import of the qualification must always be borne in mind. Only persons obsessed with the unjustifiable metaphysical presupposition that all knowledge, to be genuine, must consist of 'laws' such, for example, as those of the physical sciences, will be misled by a false ideal in this regard.

3. We come, accordingly, to our third problem, namely that of determining the aim or aims of scientific inference. What it is that the natural scientist is really seeking to accomplish, what are the general distinctive criteria of scientific knowledge, are alternative formulations of this problem.

A tremendous difficulty at once presents itself, however, and threatens to render wholly unavailing any attempt to grapple objectively with such a problem. When, in the ordinary course of things, such questions arise, each philosophical school naturally assumes its own characteristic attitude, thus effectively predetermining how it will answer them. As we have already seen, not only the function but the very nature of induction and deduction, in relation to inference as a whole, are differently construed by different schools of thought. And now we are about to find that whether science merely presents a 'description' or offers an 'explanation' of its subject matter, to say nothing of different definitions of these two terms, is equally a controversial issue.

On the one hand—to repeat—such divergences merely reflect more deeply seated differences of philosophical conviction. Thus, Meyerson's thesis that the aim of science is to explain phenomena and not merely to describe them, summed up in his famous formula that 'to explain' is 'to identify,' forms an integral part of his philosophical doctrine that in the process of 'identification' the essential nature of the thought-activity fully and adequately expresses itself. In exact antithesis to this view Karl Pearson's philosophical positivism finds its characteristic expression in the statement that scientific laws (e.g., Newton's law of gravitation) "simply *describe*, they never *explain* the routine of our perceptions, the sense impressions we project into an 'outside' world."[10] In these cases, of course, the writers are speaking, not as scientists, but

[10] Karl Pearson, *The Grammar of Science*, 3rd ed., p. 99.

as philosophers or metaphysicians, and consequently their declarations may not seem to be of much importance to any one else.

On the other hand, the scientist himself, in so far as he is more than a routine specialist, and however much he may pride himself upon his decision to abjure all metaphysics, must give some attention to Professor Whitehead's authoritative assertion that the answer to the question as to the aims of scientific investigation "even when merely implicit in the scientific imagination, must profoundly affect the development of every science."[11] One has only to consider the divergent results springing from differences of attitude on the part of scientists as such, precisely when they are ostensibly striving to be most thoroughly 'scientific,' towards the process of evolution in biology, or the theory of relativity in physics, or the foundations of mathematics, in order to appreciate something of the significance of this thesis.

These illustrations of the meaning for science and ultimate implications for philosophy of such various attitudes, merely serve as proof of the existence of the attitudes themselves, but unfortunately do not suggest how we are to deal with them. Are we arbitrarily to choose that point of view among those already represented, which seems to us most plausible? Support for this procedure could easily be drawn from the several sciences themselves, as witness the enviable success of M. Meyerson and Professor Cassirer in sustaining and corroborating their widely divergent conclusions. Or

[11] Whitehead, *Principles of Natural Knowledge,* p. 1.

are we to put forward a claim for originality by proposing still another possibility? This would be an easy way to acquire a temporary reputation for philosophical profundity, and apparent novelty is always sure to attract some enthusiastic adherents and supporters. Merely to state these alternatives, however, is enough to demonstrate their subjective origin and thorough irrationality. Ultimately our only resource seems to consist in the possibility of an appeal to those rather general propositions already laid down in the preceding chapter. Can we discover in them an objective basis for a tenable resolution of these difficulties?

The method of natural science, we declared, is the only reliable procedure by which to acquire a knowledge of the 'external' world. In the present connection this means that the problem of discovering the aim of science is one and the same with the problem of determining more specifically the fundamental characteristics of natural knowledge. It is all very well to say that the formal, methodological assumption that nature 'behaves' in a definite manner, and according to rationally comprehensible laws, is the necessary and sufficient justification of the behavior of those who devote their lives to a study of natural phenomena. This, after all, is only to repeat a very old and standard refrain, namely that knowledge implies system and system unity. But the really interesting problem still awaits solution. For there are systems and systems, unities of various kinds and of all degrees. There is the unity of a natural object, of a stone or of an organism; in another sense, perhaps, a family or a state manifests institutional unity; and any legal argument or historical exposition is, in some sense of the word, systematic.

Obviously, what we now have to determine is the specific meaning of system and unity as applied to scientific knowledge. And here we have a good opportunity to test the value and significance, for a student of logic, of the historically attested achievements in this domain. How else, if not by recourse to the actual histories of the several sciences, may we expect to arrive at an impartial formulation of the aims of scientific reasoning? Accordingly we turn to one of the best as well as one of the most familiar illustrations of the development of natural knowledge, namely the work of Copernicus, Kepler, Galileo and Newton.

Copernicus no doubt deserves the title of pioneer in the modern development of astronomy. And his emphasis upon simplicity, consistency, and the significance of mathematics, represents a great step in advance from the point of view of the logic of science. In order to appreciate this fact we have only to recall that for generations students had conducted their very limited examinations of nature in the light of certain conceptions of the aim of knowledge derived from their rather imperfect understanding of Aristotle's logic. This means that classification was to them the fundamental form of knowledge, and hence they were satisfied intellectually with a fixed division of natural objects and processes into genera, species, and individuals. On this view

> . . . nothing is presupposed save the existence of things in their inexhaustible multiplicity, and the power of the mind to select from this wealth of particular existences those features that are *common* to several of them. When we thus collect objects characterized by possession of some common property into classes, and when we repeat this process upon higher levels, there gradually arises an ever firmer order and division of being, according to the series of factual similarities running through the particular things. The essential functions of thought, in this connection, are merely those of comparing and differentiating a sensuously given manifold . . . the peculiar merit of this interpretation seems to be that it never destroys or imperils the *unity* of the ordinary view of the world.[12]

In this respect even mathematics stood on a par with the other sciences, for the concept of a plane rectangular figure was formed by abstracting from the square, the rectangle, the rhomboid, the rhombus, the trapezium, etc., the common properties, which could be immediately apprehended and pointed out.

This unity, however, based as it is on a formal rule for the formation of the generic concept, contains within itself no guarantee that it will bear a significant relation to the particulars subsumed under it. Lotze somewhere cites as an example of the weakness implicit in classification, regarded as a satisfaction of the impulse to know, the grouping together of meat and cherries under the common rubrics: red, juicy, and edible.

Now Copernicus also regarded the world as a unity, but as a unity which he characterized as a Pythagorean harmony of the spheres. In other words, Copernicus

[12] Cassirer, *op. cit.,* p. 5.

substituted for the qualitative unity of the world, with its sharp distinctions between heavenly and terrestrial phenomena, a mathematical or quantitative unity in terms of a certain kind of motion. And it is just this idea which Kepler takes up and develops. As a result of his work the idea comes to clear expression that all genuine knowledge of nature is mathematical or quantitative. Aided on the one hand by his own brilliant work in mathematics, and on the other by the precise empirical observations of Tycho Brahe, he succeeded in establishing the fact that the best way of saving the astronomical appearances was on the hypothesis of elliptical orbits with the sun at one of the foci. And although in his thought there was still a very confused blending of theological, æsthetic, and scientific interests, he nevertheless defined in a new way the notion of unity in the sense in which it applies to a body of scientific knowledge.

Gone now, forever, is the teleological theory that heavenly bodies move in circles because circular motion is 'best'; gone are the cumbrous and more and more preposterous systems of cycles and epicycles to explain the apparent irregularities in the motion of the planets; gone is the sharp distinction between heavenly and terrestrial phenomena. Henceforth man will seek to embrace the entire physical universe within a single system, based upon one or more comprehensive principles, capable of simple and elegant mathematical expression.

In this way, through the work of Kepler, and even more through the work and influence of Galileo, the conception of natural law, as we understand it to-day, quickly impressed itself upon scientists and philosophers alike. Nature, Galileo concisely declares, is "inexorable," acts only through immutable laws which she never transgresses.[13] The influence of such metaphysical pronouncements, and the rapid progress of the physical sciences which conclusively confirmed them, naturally induced a hostile attitude towards the previously dominant modes of thought. Indeed, so pervasive and insistent has this conception of science as essentially consisting in the search for laws become, that from time to time we find students of 'the social sciences' valiantly endeavoring to formulate the laws of social phenomena. So much law, so much science, seems to be one of those obviously self-evident presuppositions which it were a waste of time even to put into words, much less to discuss.

Moreover, students of the logic of science are constantly pointing out the weaknesses of classification as compared with law, and especially the weakness which resides in the fact that an exception, which refuses to come under the common rule of division, may be so easily disposed of. The temptation immediately arises to formulate a more abstract class name in order then to assign the new particular to a sub-class thus simply created for it. The final result of such a process would be that the more comprehensive the range of our intellectual vision the less effectively would it penetrate the outer shell of the particular object or phenomenon.

[13] Quoted by Burtt, *The Metaphysical Foundations of Modern Physics*, p. 64.

For the notion of nature as the expression of law, on the other hand, the exception is a problem which cannot be met by any such subterfuge. Either the exception—or discrepancy—must prove the 'rule,' so to speak, by finding its place as a member of a system of differentiated but interrelated elements, or the rule, the law, must be modified to an indeterminate extent.

There are, however, various forms of classification and various kinds of laws, and to be strictly accurate we must modify the above assertion in the light of this important qualification. It is true that the earliest, simplest mode of classification is based upon one or more immediately observable attributes, and may therefore join together in the same group objects possessing little real similarity of nature. The emphasis at this stage tends to fall on the practical purposes which the objects or events might subserve, and such a pragmatic criterion is external; results, as we say, in an artificial classification. But in due course of time the disinterestedness characteristic of pure science replaces practical need as an attitude towards things, and classification simultaneously becomes more and more objective, more 'natural.' Content at first with a few superficial attributes, the logical ideal of a modern, scientific classification is to include as its basis all of the important attributes of a group of objects.

Modern biology furnishes one of the most interesting illustrations of this point. Linnæus first chose the sexual organs, since they were easily distinguishable, as a primary character for his classification of plants. Later he classified the animal kingdom according to internal structure, and characterized animals according to the heart and the blood. This was a first step towards a comprehension of the orderliness immanent in a great domain, but even Linnæus himself recognized the artificiality and arbitrariness of the selection of the characters upon which his system rested. A more natural system resulted from the labors of de Jussieu, whose *Genera Plantarum* (1789) introduced the principle of arranging plants "according to the relations which they exhibit and according to the totality of their organization."[14]

Closely paralleling this distinction between artificial, or pragmatic, and natural classification, is the distinction between empirical and explanatory laws. Many empirical laws are hardly more than pragmatic rules, such as were already known to the science of ancient times. Explanatory laws, however, belong distinctively to modern times, and, like natural classification, presuppose, while they transcend in objectivity and knowledge-value, the more elementary forms.

Let us take, for example, Kepler's three laws of motion, which are obviously empirical, and Newton's law of gravitation, which is as plainly of the explanatory type. The difference between these two types is

[14] Merz, *History of European Thought in the XIXth Century,* Vol. II, p. 235. There are many other sciences, such as ethnology, which to-day continue to seek for more fundamental, more natural principles of classification, and especially notable in this regard are the biological sciences. Such systematic organization as these sciences are able to display presupposes the application of a vast amount of technical skill to methodical investigation, incidentally involving recourse to knowledge and principles borrowed from other sciences, especially the physical sciences.

not merely one of generality; the really important point is that the former can be regarded as a necessary consequence of the latter. In Newton's theory the ellipse functions no longer merely as a descriptive representation of the orbit of Mars,

> but we survey at a glance the whole field of "possible" orbits. The Newtonian concept of a centripetal force, that diminishes according to the square of the distance, leads to a perfect disjunction of the empirical cases in general . . . the magnitude of the initial velocity of a moving body decides—independently of the direction of the velocity—whether the form of its path is to be an ellipse or a hyperbola or a parabola. Thus the law of gravitation contains in itself the field of facts, which it rules, and ascribes strict division to its field; while the merely empirical rule of planetary motion allows the particular cases to stand in loose conjunction without sharp delimitation. . . . If we conceive the motion of the planets to be determined by gravitational forces, which work in the inverse square of the distance, then it is evident that the form of a conic section is *necessary* for their path.

Of course we must remember that this determination really holds with regard to the kind and magnitude of attraction, only "through the methodic necessity of the power of this assumption to unify observations and to give them definite meaning."[15] Other examples of the same kind include the kinetic theory of gases, which 'explains' Boyle's, Avogadro's, and Gay-Lussac's laws; and the wave theory of light, from which the law of refraction may be deduced. These more general laws are perhaps more properly called principles, as, e.g., the relativity principle, or—sometimes—theories, as in the above examples. In short, the rela-

[15] Cassirer, *op. cit.,* pp. 258, 259.

tion of a theory or a principle to an empirical law is analogous to the relation of the latter to the particular facts of observation and experiment.[16]

Thus the arrangement of objects in a class, and the formulation of a law expressing the relationships or behavior of objects, turn out to be two quite distinguishable results of scientific activity—though, to be sure, both laws and classes imply some more ultimate theoretical conceptions and principles as their systematic foundation and logical justification. In modern science, as we have seen, the tendency is to overlook this fact, and to insist on the doctrine that

[16] We may just note in passing certain other, less important classifications which cut across our classification of laws. Following Professor Wolf, we may distinguish between laws of coexistence and laws of sequence. "There is a law of coexistence, whenever a number of attributes or states are regularly together. In the case of natural classes, for instance, certain characteristics are usually found together. Similarly, with various kinds of geometrical figures. A law of sequence consists of the regular successions of certain states or events, as, for example, between changes of temperature and changes of volume, between thunder and lightning, between the seasons of the year and so on." (*Essentals of Scientific Method,* pp. 104, 105.) Professor Lalande carries the analysis still further. In his interesting book on *Théories de l'induction et de l'expérimentation* (p. 187), he lists no fewer than six sub-classes of laws; namely, those which give expression to: (*a*) Baconian forms: structure of the molecule, constitution of the atom, kinetic theory of gases, cellular theory; (*b*) numerical relationships, connecting measurable magnitudes of the type y = (f)x: gravitation, refraction, relation between the electromotive force, the resistance and the intensity of a current; (*c*) the determination of numerical constants: velocity of light, wave lengths, specific heats, atomic weights; (*d*) permanent *liaison* of characters: constancy of chemical properties, anatomical dispositions, empirical concomitants such as the cloven hoof of ruminants; (*e*) repetitions of the same process: crystallization, phases of chemical reaction, stadia of embryonic development, diseases, aging and death of organisms; (*f*) vector relationships: Carnot's principle of the degradation of energy, geological and palæontological evolution.

all genuine science, when fully developed, consists of laws, modeled on those of physics. But in this work we are not concerned primarily with ideals which may or may not be realizable in practice; on the contrary we are trying to understand the actual state of affairs. And from this point of view there can be no question: in certain sciences classification is at present the principal activity, and hence we must either deny to such sciences the claim to independence and genuineness, or relinquish the fashionable doctrine. And if nothing else will determine which alternative to select, then there is one most important consideration which will render the decision unequivocally.

This consideration is to the effect that the class and the law, respectively, regard the individual, the particular, from two quite different points of view. For the latter the particular is only an instance, an example, of the validity of the law. Certain abstract attributes are separated from the others, and then taken, for the purposes of experimental inquiry, as including all that is essential in the object. Whatever other attributes or properties it may possess are, for the time being, and from the point of view of the problems involved, extraneous and meaningless. Thus an object or phenomenon loses its individuality to a very considerable extent, and becomes, instead, one of an indefinite host of remarkably similar entities. With regard to the individual and the species, on the other hand, the very fact that the "totality of the organization" is what counts in distinguishing members of one species from those of another, is enough to allow for a very considerable degree of uniqueness—indicated by peculiarities of structure and function, or otherwise—especially in the case of the more complex organisms. We shall have occasion to come back to this point presently.[17]

We are now seemingly in a position to discuss more intelligently the question as to the aim or aims of scientific investigation. Still keeping in mind such developments as that from Copernicus to Newton, and that from Linnæus to his successors, together with the distinction between class and law, we may hope to dispose of the argument as to whether science only 'describes' or really 'explains' the phenomena of the natural order. Many thinkers, however, complicate matters at this point by introducing into the discussion the terms *how* and *why*. It will be necessary, therefore, briefly to consider this additional distinction in the light of what has preceded.

Some, arguing that *why* means reference either to intelligible purpose (teleology), or to an inferred First Cause (God), flatly deny that science has any business with such an explanation of things. Science only describes *how* things as a matter of fact do happen; it neither can nor cares to raise any further issues. And they may even cite Newton's inconsistent views on this point as proof of their contention. When Newton made the famous remark, *hypotheses non fingo*, he clearly had in mind the extraneous 'metaphysical' and theological speculations of his predecessors and contemporaries. On the other hand, Newton himself was

[17] Cf. below, Chapter VI.

guilty of this very same practice, for did he not speak of the world as God's sensorium? And do we not owe to him, preëminently, the conception of the world as a great machine, constructed and set running by God?[18]

The truth of the matter is that in their elation over the remarkable successes of the physical sciences in the early modern period, scientists and philosophers alike forgot the severe limitations and restrictions implicit in the scientific method and presuppositions, and considered that they had only to supplement 'natural philosophy' by a little theology in order to reveal, to explain the workings, the plan, and the purpose, of the great world-machine.

Nowadays, however, aware of these limitations, and more modest in their pretensions, all good positivists and empiricists will humbly acknowledge the fact that science—and all genuine knowledge is scientific—can only *describe* how things take place or behave.

Other thinkers, however, while still admitting that the word *why* is ambiguous, yet contend that science is more than a mere description; it offers in some sense what must after all be called an explanation of things. They agree with their opponents that ultimate explanation—if there be any—should be left to metaphysicians and their like. Science has nothing to say of God's relation to the world, nor of the possible efficacy of final causes. But on the other hand they point to the important distinction, to which we have alluded above, between two types of law, the empirical or

[18] For a discussion of Newton cf. Burtt, *op. cit.*

descriptive, and the theoretical or explanatory. Empirical laws do merely describe the 'how' of things; but the real problem of science is to formulate laws and theories of the other kind, to discover some theoretical basis for things. Thus *why* comes to mean, on this view, an explanation in terms of natural preconditions, or (in the sense of the word explained above) in terms of systematic organization.

At this point the argument often reduces to a mere verbal dispute; it becomes a question of what we *really* mean by 'description' and what by 'explanation.' Or else certain metaphysical presuppositions are allowed to becloud the issue, as in the case of Meyerson and others. All things considered, and if we must choose a word, explanation seems preferable to description as a term to indicate the aim of science. There undeniably is a difference between artificial classifications and empirical laws, lacking any precise theoretical foundation, on the one hand, and natural classifications and explanatory laws more or less directly deducible from some systematic theory or principle, on the other hand. But if we are to use such a term, certain things must be borne in mind.

First of all, a scientific explanation is not in any sense ultimate. In the language of an earlier day, science neither requires nor attempts to prove the existence of a Supreme Being, or of final causes above and beyond the natural order. To put essentially the same truth in the language of our own day, science—natural science—neither does nor can take any cognizance of values. Values belong to the domain of experience as a whole; they involve the relation of man to his fellows and of mankind to the totality of things. And natural science, as we have shown, deliberately abstracts from any such totality, in order to concentrate its attention on that fractional part of experience commonly denominated the external world. This being its presupposition, whatever 'explanation' science has to offer cannot embrace more than a fragment—even if a very important fragment—of concrete reality.

In the second place, most thinkers, in discussing this question of the aim of science, have oversimplified the issue. By science they have meant, primarily, the physical sciences, and therefore, either implicitly or explicitly, they have assumed that all genuine natural science must aim at the one sort of explanation or description. But this is to leave out of account any specific differences that there may be between such sciences, say, as mathematics, physics, and biology. To get around this objection, some authorities would deny that mathematics is a natural science, and would maintain that ultimately the biological sciences must seek the same type of answers to their problems, as satisfy the physicists. This reply, however, without detailed evidence to support it, is open to the charge of begging the question. And we may say in anticipation that such evidence as we have been able to muster all tends to controvert this position. There are good reasons why we should regard mathematics as a natural science, and there are specific differences—what Meyerson would call "irrationalities"—which clearly distinguish the biological sciences from the physical sciences. Merely from the point of view of a logical classification of judgments, and not to anticipate what we hope to bring out in the following chapters, interesting comparisons may be made between a general mathematical proposition, a physical law, and a classificatory statement.

In principle, a mathematical proposition, like all other scientific judgments, is hypothetical in form. *If* or *given* so and so, *then* such and such follows. This hypothetical character is due, of course, to the general abstractness of science, as evidenced in its presuppositions; and also to the special limitations or aspects of its subject matter, of which any particular science takes cognizance.

But the relation which obtains between the antecedent and the consequent of mathematical judgments is of that particular type denominated ground and consequence. This relationship is sometimes misleadingly described as logical, as contrasted with factual or causal or what not. Properly speaking, of course, all genuine relationships are logical, and that of ground and consequence is one type, of which there are many others. What is peculiar about this particular type is the fact that it is timeless, involving as it does only the quantitative or formal attributes of things.

A physical law, the expression of the orderliness of material phenomena, events, processes or structure, is, at least apparently, more difficult to describe in analogous terms. But so far as explanatory principles and theories—in the sense in which we have been using these terms—are concerned, and in spite of much recent agitation on the subject, there is much to be said in favor of treating them as exemplifications of the relationship of causality. On this view cause is the set of conditions, past or present, most intimately involved in the coming to be of the result. And here, contrary to the case of mathematics, a temporal element, such as simultaneity or succession, seems always to have a place.

As for the classificatory judgment, as it functions in the biological sciences, we note at once that it differs essentially from both of the two preceding types of judgment. The relationship to which it gives expression is that of the individual to the class. As we have already pointed out, the element of individuality becomes much more prominent than in the case of physical laws. In the latter case each particular counts only as another instance of the universal; in the former, we have the recognition of variability and adaptiveness, signs and indications of considerable inner diversity of structure and function, even amongst the members of the same species. And an explanation, in this realm, means the tracing of an evolutionary process of change, and possibly reference to purpose.

The following chapters may be regarded as so many amplifications of this brief indication of some of the more important differences between the various groups of sciences.

CHAPTER III

THE MATHEMATICAL SCIENCES

THE story of the inscription over the door of Plato's Academy may be merely a pleasant tale, but there is no uncertainty as to its moral. Ignorance of mathematics and its ways is indeed responsible for much poor philosophy. Moreover, mathematics is often held up as the model for every other science to imitate, and is commonly supposed to exemplify clarity, accuracy, cogency, and conclusiveness of reasoning to a degree attained or attainable in no other sphere of mental activity. 'So much mathematics, so much science,' is a formula representing no small part of the instructed opinion of mankind from the seventeenth century down to the present day.

A little reflection on the history of the science reveals, however, a most curious state of affairs. Prior to the time of Kant scientists and philosophers were unanimously agreed that mathematical knowledge was indubitable; was, in short, ideal knowledge realized. In content the science consisted of self-evident truths, intuitively apprehended axioms, and the results following deductively and inevitably from them. Hume's skepticism might be likened to a rush of mighty waters, easily engulfing or contemptuously undermining all that ordinarily passed for *terra firma* knowledge; but it drew back, checked and appeased, before the seemingly invincible rock of the science of numbers. And Kant himself could point to Euclidean geometry as a science that had maintained its essential integrity for two thousand years.

So much for space, time, and number—a convenient phrase summarily indicating for a Kantian the content of mathematics. As to form and method, it was agreed almost unanimously that mathematical demonstration or deduction was the type to which all inference or reasoning (including philosophical) should strive to conform. Although, even prior to Mill, some thinkers occupied themselves with the logic of induction or the analysis of the so-called inductive methods, induction was generally regarded as a merely preliminary process, which a certain complexity of subject matter made it necessary to employ in certain fields other than mathematics. But that mathematics itself need ever stoop to such artifices no one even imagined. And that at best induction can give us only probable knowledge, not the absolutely certain knowledge to be had in mathematics, was a natural corollary to this view of the nature and import of inductive methodology.

Even the discovery, early in the nineteenth century, of hyperbolic (Lobatschefskian) and elliptic (Riemannian) geometries resulted in little change in this regard. Indeed, what seemed to impress thinkers as most significant, from a logical point of view, in this connection, was that they should have to formulate a new conception of the content of the science. From the comfortable, old-fashioned and complacent view that the axioms of geometry were self-evident, absolutely certain and eternal truths, revealing the real nature of the actual space-world, the intellectual fashions went to the other extreme, seemingly forced to such a position by the dead weight of events. Instead of the ancient but eminently respectable garments which even a Hume hesitated to suggest were in need of any serious alterations, the axioms of mathematics suddenly found themselves shorn of their ample robes and forced, on pain of utter nakedness as the horrible alternative, to adopt the scanty covering—hastily designed by tailor Poincaré *et al.*—rather unsatisfactorily described as 'conventional.'

In plain words, many mathematicians and logicians came to the conclusion that the axioms—or as it is now fashionable to say, the postulates—of Euclidean and non-Euclidean geometry differed, not with respect to their truth or falsity, but merely with respect to their greater or less simplicity and convenience. Curiously enough, the only science which had at all resisted the attacks of the skeptical Hume was coming of its own initiative to be skeptical of itself—at least so far as its content is concerned! Are we not accustomed to hearing mathematicians quote, with entire approval, the inimitable remark of Mr. Russell to the effect that "mathematics may be defined as the subject in which we never know what we are talking about, nor whether what we are saying is true"?

In short, we are no longer to understand that the business of mathematics is to tell us anything about the real world—about the nature of actual space, say —but rather that its sole function is to discover what are the formally correct conclusions which follow from a set of arbitrary postulates according to thoroughly abstract rules of operation. The postulates in turn merely specify what are the conditions which we may choose to impose upon certain undefined ideas, relations, and operations, in order to establish a self-consistent basis for an abstract deductive system.

Thus, for example, Hilbert has shown how to assign to the terms, 'point,' 'line,' 'plane,' etc., various 'arbitrary' properties depending upon certain prescribed conditions of relationship between the entities in question. Whether or not the results deduced from such a set of postulates have any connection with the properties of perceptual space is merely a matter of 'applied mathematics,' with which 'pure mathematics' has no concern.

It would not, of course, be true to say that all mathematicians to-day share this view of the arbitrary, conventional, gamelike character of their science,[1] but it is safe to say that this is as nearly a correct representation of the actual state of affairs as any merely general statement is likely to be. And the comparatively recent development of the theory of aggregates has served, in some quarters at least, to accentuate this view.

This theory grew out of two considerations, one logical, the other mathematical.

Bolzano had noted, as a singular circumstance, perhaps worthy of some investigation, certain paradoxical

[1] For example, Brouwer and Weyl oppose this view very strenuously. Cf. the interesting article on "Science, Philosophy and Certainty," by Professor Sheldon, in *The Philosophical Review,* Vol. XXXIX, No. 3, pp. 243-257.

properties of infinite magnitudes—for example, the fact of the 'equivalence' of an infinite aggregate with a proper part of itself. By what proved to be a stroke of genius Cantor simply set about the task of establishing a systematic foundation for the realm of the 'transfinite'; a foundation derived from its own properties and laws, among which he included this paradoxical property of equivalence.

But the principal impulse to the researches which led to the formulation of the theory nevertheless came from purely mathematical difficulties. These difficulties are too technical to admit of description here, but the interesting point for us to note is, that Cantor was able to resolve them through the formulation of this theory. We may note also that Cantor's work led to a new definition of a continuum, such as a line, in terms of discrete elements of the number-system. And thence arose the ambitious project of effecting a genuine fusion of arithmetic and geometry—a movement towards the arithmetization of pure mathematics, as it has been called. This movement ultimately and inevitably led, in turn, to a new consideration of the philosophico-mathematical problem of the ultimate basis of the concept of number itself.

Now while these important developments were transpiring in the domain of mathematics, an interesting parallel movement was working itself out in formal logic—largely through the labors of mathematicians. Boole and De Morgan became interested in the possibility of the symbolic representation of the operations of thought in general, and of the expression of the laws of thought in terms of formulæ analogous to those of algebra and arithmetic. Later, in Germany, Schroeder produced his *Algebra der Logik* (1890-1895), and many works on the same subject soon followed. It is well known that no less a thinker than Josiah Royce interested himself actively in these problems, while the culmination of the whole movement was due to the labors of the authors of *Principia Mathematica.*

This work is an ambitious attempt to assimilate in a single deductive system, and to establish on one foundation formal logic and pure mathematics—to make the parallel developments in the two fields actually coincide. What makes the work so attractive to many students is the fact that it apparently combines and gives expression to the ideals of various earlier workers on the foundations and methods of mathematics. Thus it accepts as its own the notion that the science should be based on a small number of the simplest possible conceptions, definitions, and axioms or postulates, and, in fact, assumes this as the ultimate ideal of all logical thinking. Crediting Cantor with having led the way to a definitive clarification and solution of the mathematical and philosophical problems of infinity and continuity, these thinkers seek and claim to have found an ultimate basis for the theory of aggregates in the 'logical' conception of a 'class.' And since for them all 'logical' conceptions are the products of pure thought, operating *in abstracto*, mathematics may now claim to have realized the goal for which it has long been struggling. It can now make good its claims, free from all encumbrances of a sensuous nature, to stand forth as a completely formal, logico-deductive science, operating by means of thought's own laws, and as the exemplar *par excellence* of the highest achievements of the human intellect when left to its own devices and allowed to employ its own resources in perfect freedom.[2]

All this is doubtless very inspiring—but the question the critical logician must ask is, is it real, or is it only a dream, a fond idealistic vision? As a matter of hard fact this doctrine, this enticing theory of mathematical logic, this intellectual El Dorado, has been and still is being subjected to criticisms from various quarters and in the light of various considerations.

From the side of the mathematicians the validity of Cantor's conception of transfinite numbers has been very seriously questioned; so thoroughly so that it is obvious to an impartial observer that the significance of infinity—mathematical and philosophical—is by no means definitively determined once and for all.[3] Neither is it at all clear that continuity is an unambiguous term in present-day thought. One suspects that the technically defined mathematical continuum has been confused, in some quarters, with what we mean by continuity in the most general, comprehensive sense of the word.[4] At any rate it is obviously not safe to take

[2] Even the mathematical logicians themselves seem, however, to have some doubts on this score, as witness the various rather definite qualifications and restrictions in the second edition of *Principia Mathematica.*

[3] Cf. E. W. Hobson, *The Theory of Functions,* etc.

[4] Cf. the present writer's *The Philosophical Presuppositions of Mathematical Logic.*

it for granted, as the mathematical logicians generally do, that the two meanings coincide. Again, many contemporary mathematicians and logicians (e.g., Cassirer) find in the conception of a class a serious ambiguity—i.e., that its definition is circular, in that it presupposes the very concept of number for which it is supposed to serve as a basis.

And, finally, from the side of logic, it may be seriously questioned whether the nature of the process of deduction has been grasped completely by those who are the chief exponents of the view that mathematics is a purely deductive science. May not their explicit admission of their failure to understand how induction in the physical sciences is possible really suggest that they only think they understand the process of deduction, even in mathematics? It might easily be argued that all other current misconceptions and disagreements among those working at the foundations of mathematics have their principal source in the uncritically accepted doctrine of its wholly deductive character. It is now generally understood that Descartes, for example, in an earlier age, cannot be said to have grasped the true nature of mathematical inference.

The preceding considerations set the twofold task for this and the following chapter. On the one hand, the radical denial that mathematics has any specific subject matter threatens to deprive the science of all significant content, and to render inexplicable both its ready and extensive applicability to the problems of the physical sciences, and also the fact that such sciences often propose problems that suggest further developments in pure mathematics. It is accordingly to the interest of scientist and philosopher alike that an attempt be made to overcome this apparent epistemological dualism between the world of purely abstract and arbitrary thought constructions and the world of concrete natural phenomena. And on the other hand there is a no less important and correlative problem of methodology demanding solution. That the 'mathematical method' is a distinct form of inference, differing radically from inference in other fields of knowledge, both in its character as purely deductive, and in the absolute finality of its conclusions, is accepted widely as a truism. The truism needs challenging, however, for so long as it maintains itself successfully we remain unable to justify our faith in the unity of scientific thought in all its manifestations—and consequently find ourselves at a loss to explain what we mean by the features common to all scientific reasoning as such. In short, these conceptions of the content and form of mathematical reasoning tend completely to isolate the science both from the natural sciences and from philosophy, i.e., from the world of experience which sets the problems both for the other sciences and for philosophy. Hence the remainder of this chapter and all of the next chapter will be concerned primarily with an attempt to restore the significance which the science has theoretically lost, but which it has never in practice relinquished, relatively to the actual world of experience, while at the same time we must seek, of course, to preserve the elements of truth implicit in the developments outlined above.

We begin with the problem of determining anew the content, the subject matter of the science.

Many contemporary mathematicians and logicians agree in repudiating the old definition that mathematics is the science of quantity, on grounds of its inadequacy. And if by quantity we merely mean measure, in the sense of an answer to the question, 'How much,' or 'How many,' then clearly mathematics is the broader term. But originally and primarily the definition meant something more, and hence, before rejecting it *in toto*, we must try to understand it in this wider sense.[5]

Both in ordinary life and in more technical literature it is customary to distinguish quantity and the quantitative aspect of things from their quality and qualitative characteristics.[6] No doubt such distinctions usually entail no very clear conception of what they ultimately presuppose, and very few philosophers, even, ever give the matter much thought. Yet if quality and quantity do represent two distinct ways in which thought apprehends its objects—two categories —then it ought to be both possible and profitable to fix their meaning rather carefully. To this end we shall start from ordinary usage, and shall try to render our first differentiation more precise and determinate by further analysis.

[5] Cf., e.g., Green, "Quantity is simply the most elementary of the relations by which thought constitutes the real world, as detached from this world and presented by thought to itself as a separate object." *General Introduction to Hume,* p. 226.

[6] Cf., e.g., Bergson, *Matter and Memory;* Spaier, *La pensée et la quantité;* Bosanquet, *Logic.*

By the qualities of a thing we understand, in general, those properties or characteristics of it which are most directly revealed by and through our senses. Such are light, color, taste, odor, warmth or coldness, hardness, etc.—in short the 'secondary qualities' of certain philosophers.[7] In the early stages of the history of the physical sciences thinkers like Galileo adopted the view that these so-called secondary qualities were subjective, dependent upon the nature of the percipient's mental and physical constitution, while the primary qualities were objective, inherent in the nature of the objects of perception. In other words, it was tacitly assumed that secondary qualities are those implying a relationship only between the individual and the object, while the relations of objects among themselves remain undetermined or unnoticed. And hence on this view secondary qualities represent the most elementary type of apprehension of external phenomena. This doubtless explains why it is that the qualitative atomism of Anaxagoras preceded the quantitative atomism of Democritus. Even if we abandon as unsound and obsolete the distinction between primary and secondary qualities, no one can deny that simple sense qualities, colors, odors, sounds, etc., are what we learn first of the objects of experience. It is only considerably later that comparisons and distinctions between objects *qua*

[7] Incidentally, that even the perception of these supposedly immediate characteristics is no merely passive reception of them by the mind, but involves some modicum of thought-activity, seems established by the fact that for the early Greek philosophers the distinction between the qualities of a thing and the thing itself was not fully understood.

objects come explicitly to be made, and that we begin to apprehend them in terms of their so-called primary qualities, i.e., in terms of their simplest relations to each other, as well as in terms of their more immediate sensuous characteristics. A vast amount of data procured from investigation of the language and reckonings of savage tribes all over the world has clearly established the validity of this thesis. Suppose, by way of illustration, that we take the case of number.

These investigations not only prove the sensuous origin of number, they tell us also something about the nature of quantitative determination in general. The ability to count, even small numbers, is only slowly acquired, and the manner in which this development takes place reveals the various elements which go to make up the number-concept. These elements are, of course, unity, plurality, and sum or totality.

In the most elementary stages of thought and language, however, such distinctions are lacking. What we call the number '2,' for example, is, for an early stage of civilization, a dual, and, as such, little more than a directly perceived natural fact or quality of an object. Authorities tell us that here and there in various languages, Sanskrit, Greek, Teutonic, Semitic, etc., we meet with this concept of duality, or special grammatical form intended to express the fact that certain things possess the quality of duplication. In other words, duality in so far only amounts to a particular sensuous attribute of things, practically or quite on a par with other qualities—color, odor, etc. A further development in the same direction leads to the idea of a more or less indefinite plurality. Even in Greek and Latin the plural has a distinct meaning of its own; it is not regarded as the definitive multiple of a single unit. In such cases, originally, plurals (and collectives) plainly indicate a stage of thought and language wherein an aggregate of singular units function simply as a uniquely qualitied example of the object. Our words, 'flock,' 'herd,' 'fleet,' etc., still reflect the way in which number in general, or rather plurality, remains limited to and hampered by a special class of objects. In all such cases number is characterized by the quality of the objects to which it refers; numbers are class words. The well-known distinction between numbers in the abstract, or as such (1,2,3,4), and physical numbers (2 men, 4 stones), is only less significant in this connection than the geometrical classification of numbers as square, oblong, etc., and the Pythagorean thesis that things are numbers.[8]

From the indefinite 'many' the human mind was able to rise only very slowly and by degrees to the conception of definite sums or totals, while the distinction between large groups of objects of slightly different number was for long apprehended as a merely qualitative one. But as the definite meaning of plurality and of sum or totality as the synthesis of plurality and unity becomes clearer, it is obvious that vast generaliza-

[8] "It is a commonplace to mathematicians," remarks Professor Burtt, "that save for the last two centuries during which higher algebra has to a considerable extent freed men's minds from dependence on spatial representations in their mathematical thinking, geometry has always been the mathematical science *par excellence.*" *Metaphysical Foundations of Modern Physical Science,* p. 29. Cf. also *ibid.,* pp. 30-33 and the works there referred to.

tions become possible. The peculiar significance of duality gets absorbed or generalized into the concept of plurality in general, while more and more the number-concept frees itself from its immediate associations with perceptual phenomena, including, finally, space itself, and develops into a full-fledged, independent object of thought. As such, consideration is directed, not as formerly, towards number as immersed in sense-objects as a property of such objects, but rather to an investigation and development of the properties and attributes of numbers themselves—a process which is going steadily forward at the present time.[9]

[9] It may be worth while in this connection briefly to recall certain further steps in the history of the science of number. The simplest type of number is the positive whole number, the series of so-called natural numbers. In the Middle Ages India contributed an important addition to this series in the form of zero. The significance of this conception, both for arithmetic and geometry, it would be hard to over-emphasize. Not until the seventeenth century—i.e., after about four centuries of conflict—did the negative numbers gain unquestioned recognition. This development made possible the unlimited generality of the process of subtraction. Similarly the next great extension—that of fractional numbers—rendered a like service for the process of division. Besides the whole and fractional positive and negative numbers, which are together defined as "rational," another new type was introduced, called "irrational." These numbers answered to several demands, which rational numbers could not satisfy, such as the problems of generalizing the process of extracting the square root, so that every positive rational number could be said to have a root, whether it were a "square" number or not; of numerically determining the relation of the diameter of a circle to its circumference, and of the diagonal to a side of a quadrilateral. And the general concept of an "irrational" number was developed in several different ways, by Dedekind, by Heine, Cantor, and Méray, and by Weierstrass. Another extension of the number-concept is the "imaginary" number. These numbers are the square roots of negative numbers. So far these new types of numbers obey laws of which the laws for

Now these facts, considered as mere historical data, are of no especial consequence. But from the point of view of our present study they are of great significance. For these or similar developments are typical of every science. Every science arises out of particular determinations of sense phenomena, and in the course of its history frees itself by degrees from these narrow limitations, until, by successive analyses, generalizations, and new applications, the science becomes conscious of its own subject matter—a subject matter which is thought, conceptualized, rather than sensuously presented. In other words a science becomes such just in and as a result of the process of defining its objects conceptually, and when it is definitely apprehended that the objects with which it is concerned are no mere sensuous appearances, but genuine thought-determinations of such appearances.

Such determinations—the fundamental conceptions of a science—are, as we say, the products of thought, and no mere sensuous data. And so it seems that Plato was right when he declared that number first awakens the intelligence, and reveals the infinite possibilities of thought to transcend the limitations of immediate sense experience. Number, we may say, is the first thought, at least in the scientific sense of the word; that is, the

operations with natural numbers may be regarded as specializations. But finally, in still more recent extensions of the number-concept, such as Cantor's "transfinite" numbers, of infinite aggregates of different powers, the laws of operation diverge essentially from the former, as is also the case with quarternions, and other higher complex numbers, and the non-Archimedian numbers. But here we reach the stage of questionable validity and controversy, the outposts of contemporary discussion.

first thought derived from man's experience of external phenomena and systematically developed.

So far, then, we may claim to have traced, very briefly and inadequately, the logical genesis of the concept of number. We have been following, so to speak, a gradual process ultimately dependent upon the logical development and clarification of the distinction between the quantitative aspect of things and their more immediate sensuous qualities. But now, with this realization that number is a thought, and, as such, definitively transcendent to the world of mere sense appearances, our difficulties really begin. In accordance with what seems to be an inviolable law of our thinking (possibly the law of least resistance), what began as a harmless distinction between thought and sense directly transforms itself into a hard and fast antithesis or opposition. Pure mathematics—such, it will be remembered, is the contention of many thinkers—whatever its origin, and however much it may have been dependent upon experience, intuition or what not, in the past, has no longer anything to do with the phenomenal world; the conceptions of mathematics are not derived from contact with physical things as are the conceptions of the other sciences, but are the products of pure thought, operating, according to some extremists, with formal symbols, blank counters devoid of experiential significance. And yet, as was briefly indicated above, the absolute separation between mathematical conceptions and the phenomenal order, implied in this last statement, cannot easily be reconciled with certain other very important considerations.

There is, first, the fact that certain important advances in the very highest reaches of pure mathematics have been due to the demand for a solution of some novel problem in the physical sciences. And we may point out in passing to those thinkers who do not include geometry in the domain of pure mathematics, on the ground that in geometry our reasonings do, as in pure mathematics they do not, involve an experiential factor—space—that actually geometrical problems, like various cases of incommensurability, have stimulated the invention, and even in some instances have enforced acceptance of such numerical conceptions as irrational and imaginary numbers.

Secondly, it needs emphasizing that progress in every science means an increase in concreteness; not, as is commonly supposed, an increase in abstractness. According to a current and widespread misconception, every science, as it develops, becomes more abstract; its fundamental conceptions become less and less like anything we actually experience. Admitting that we gain in comprehensiveness, it is assumed that *ipso facto* we lose in depth; the greater the range of our knowledge the less (paradoxically enough) it tells us about any particular object or phenomenon. But a little reflection reveals that this is a mistaken view, while at the same time it is easy to see how it could arise. In a commonplace sense, of course, any conception is abstract, relatively to its source. But in the more important sense every new conception in any science helps to bind the content of the science into a more closely woven network of relationships and interconnections.

And in this way, surely, there is a gain in significance, an increase in depth as well as in extent of our knowledge. Thus instead of becoming less significant and more remote relatively to the world of phenomenal objects from which it arose, it would seem that the number-concept, as it develops, should and does apply more fully to it and at the same time reveals new meaning in it. Think, for example, of the value of $i = \sqrt{-1}$ in this regard; in addition to its applications in pure geometry and in theoretical physics we actually solve practical engineering problems through its use.

And finally, how are we to interpret the many claims that some one science, say Einsteinian physics, is reducible to some more abstract science, say geometry? Is not the element of truth in most if not all of these reductionist doctrines just that of the unlimited applicability of new thought-constructions to experience? Geometry a branch of physics, physics a branch of geometry, geometry a branch of arithmetic—what else can the logician make of these claims and counterclaims on the part of scientists?

These considerations are all neatly included in the assertion of an eminent mathematician, Professor Hobson, that every new mathematical conception must meet a twofold test, satisfy two demands. Such a conception must be shown to be self-consistent, and it must prove itself capable of some concrete interpretation, some theoretical applications.[10] The term i is

[10] Cf. Hobson, *The Domain of Natural Science;* also Bridgeman, *The Logic of Modern Physics.*

a mere symbol, a demand that a certain operation be performed, rather than a significant element in the number-system, until a way can be found for carrying out the operation indicated in terms of acceptable mathematical conceptions. Many, of course, would go much farther than this. In addition, they would urge that any valid mathematical demonstration or reasoning, however abstruse, can proceed only by the aid of 'constructions' in perceptual or imaginative intuition, involving relations which we must regard as developed from those immanent in relatively direct experience.

These facts are enough to render highly questionable the theory that pure mathematics is the product of pure thought 'creating'—as some would have it—or 'discovering'—as others prefer to say—its objects *in vacuo*. Indeed, if nothing but abstract thought following its own innate laws were responsible for these objects, it would be extremely difficult to see how either error or new knowledge could ever arise with regard to them.

Perhaps to obviate such difficulties and objections as these, some thinkers have suggested that we might distinguish mathematical objects from those of all other sciences by the use of the notion of ideality or subsistence. Ideal or subsistent are those objects which are not to be found in experience, and which lay no claim to existential reality. Obviously *i*, or any element of four-dimensional space, is such an ideal object. But apart from the ambiguity latent in such a term as experience, and in the contrast between ideality and reality, many if not all of the objects of the other sciences are also ideal. A perfect lever, frictionless motion on an inclined plane, an absolutely pure chemical substance—where are these to be had 'in experience'?

Nevertheless, there is admittedly a very real difference between these last-mentioned objects and those of mathematics. The ultimate elements of which physics finds the world to be composed may be conceptual, ideal, by hypothesis not immediately present to sense as gross objects are supposed to be; but all the same they possess attributes analogous to those assigned to sense objects, and attributes which can be accurately, if indirectly, determined by measurement. The ultimate elements with which the various branches of mathematics concern themselves, on the other hand, enjoy no such concrete substantial status. They almost seem to merit the designation of pure intellectual abstractions. And this is true, not only with regard to the conceptions foundational to non-Euclidean geometry, say, but even of so simple an idea as the number '2,' or an isosceles triangle. Thus all our endeavors to describe satisfactorily the content of mathematical science and to determine its relation to the content of the other sciences seem to result only in confusion or stalemate.

What we must try to do, in these perplexing circumstances, is to formulate a conception of the content of mathematics which will at once allow for the undoubted fact of transcendence of sense experience on the one hand, and which will at the same time enable us to recognize some sort of connection between mathematical objects and perceptual objects.

At this point the idea of quantity may after all prove of assistance. Perhaps we shall discover, in this old-fashioned notion, the object of scorn and derision at the hands of certain of our wise contemporaries, the only satisfactory clue to a solution of our problem. In the light of our earlier account of the genesis of the science of number, mathematics as the science of quantity has to do with those most abstract and simple aspects of perceptual objects which depend only on the event of their being also objects of thought. To be perceptual, objects must in principle be capable of possessing sensuous qualities; and to be objects of thought, universalized, they must be capable of being invested with interrelations of one sort or another. Not that perception and thought are two separate mental processes; it would be more accurate to say that the latter is simply a development of the former. And in fact it is in terms of some such considerations as these that not a few students of the logic of science have sought to understand the content of the science of mathematics, and the relation of this content to experience.

In his latest work on the philosophy of science, *La déduction relativiste*, for example, Meyerson observes that "quality as such appears to us as something complete in itself; not only in that, in so far as existent, it postulates nothing beyond itself, but also in that it is something intensive and therefore not susceptible of combining with, or of relating [adding] itself to anything else; this privilege being in fact what characterizes quantity and what distinguishes it from quality." . . . In an operation like addition, for example, "the identity which serves as a point of departure is preserved, while nevertheless the diversity of the result is patent." It follows that "the world of quantity, as compared with that of quality, may be conceived of as being in flux, and as analogous in consequence, from this point of view, to the reality presented in sensation, but as nevertheless capable of serving to explain—in a certain measure, of course—the incessant flux of the latter."[11] Here we have a broad hint of the true sense in which quantity 'transcends' (and partially includes) quality, and also an indication of the content and aim of the science of mathematics.

And another writer, Spaier, in his instructive work on *La pensée et la quantité*, also confirms and further illustrates the same thesis.

> M. Bergson [declares Spaier] has very conclusively demonstrated that "time" is . . . a conceptual elaboration of a complex . . . qualitative datum. The space of the adult, the geometrician, and the philosopher, is also an abstraction of the same type; the work of thought has made of space a quantity.

But be it noted that we are not to conclude from such facts as these that quantity has no connection with reality; on the contrary, quantity is a

> . . . synthesis—well-justified by the only two criteria at our disposal, agreement with experience and intelligibility [Cf. Hobson's remarks, above]—of actually observable properties . . . the homogeneity of most qualities induces us to arrange

[11] Meyerson, *La déduction relativiste*, pp. 11, 12.

these qualities in collections . . . classes. And secondly the periodicity of phenomena as well as their extensional arrangement constrains us to establish among them order and correspondence. Now the raw material of quantity consists precisely in these colligations, this order, and these correspondences.[12]

It is just these quantitative aspects of things, construed by means of a legitimate abstraction, as independent both of all other more concrete aspects and even of the actual things themselves, that the science of mathematics is engaged in progressively specifying. The same is true, of course, *mutatis mutandis,* of the other natural sciences—every science concentrates on certain aspects of things, ignores all other more concrete aspects, and idealizes, so to speak, the aspects selected for special investigation.

This point is so important that we may allow ourselves space enough to clarify and emphasize it by means of an example. Geometry we may define, on this view, as the science of spatial relationships as such. It starts from a vague, indefinite, qualitative spatial experience, the space of common sense, and its aim is to translate this experience into intelligible quantitative relations. It can be shown that those mathematicians who apparently succeed in constructing geometry by purely rational methods do so only because they surreptitiously appropriate from experience and spatial intuition the constituent elements of space, namely those properties which make geometry a branch of mathematics distinct from a pure algebra or arith-

[12] Spaier, *La pensée et la quantité,* pp. 40, 41. Cf. also the same writer's *La pensée concrète,* pp. 383, 384.

metic. Indeed, if this content be eliminated from space *ipso facto* nothing is left of it, and it is an arbitrary procedure to give the name of geometry to the science which results from such an abstraction. Whatever we may regard as constituting the qualitative content of space, and, as such, irreducible to mere numerical relations, e.g., perhaps the diversity of positions, is what is empirical in it; while space as the mathematician conceives it is a means of making experience so far intelligible. In this sense of the word, the intelligibility of space is due to the constructive activity of thought. Dimensions, for example, are not 'given,' but are a product of the analysis made by thought, of indistinct spatial experience, in order, as we said, to translate that experience into intelligible quantitative relations.

To return from this illustration to our main point. It is especially interesting to note that according to such authorities as those we have just drawn upon there are two correlative attributes or characteristics of all quantitative (i.e., mathematical) determination: namely, externality or separateness, and homogeneity —what Hegel called the moments of discreteness and continuity. And other logicians and mathematicians confirm this doctrine. Thus, for example, Johnson explains that "when the complementary notions of separateness and togetherness are joined to constitute a unity, there enters the idea of number and we are in the domain of mathematics." [13] Similarly Sigwart declares that he has always designated separation (*Unter-*

[13] *Logic,* Vol. I, p. xxiii.

scheidung) and combination (*Zusammenfassung des Unterscheidenen*) as the two effective functions of the process of numbering.[14] What is more noteworthy still, in his analysis of numerical diversity, Russell unconsciously agrees with Hegel as to the essential characteristics of what the latter calls the domain of pure quantitative determination. In fact, it would be very difficult, indeed, to discover a thinker who did not point to homogeneity and externality, separateness, or indifference towards one another, as the two obvious attributes of mathematical objects. Students who are inclined to think of all philosophers as in fundamental disagreement with each other might be startled by the unanimity of view in this regard, once the purely verbal differences are disposed of. Spatial diversity, according to Russell, is a sufficient basis for numerical difference. And Bergson makes almost the same point, incidentally, in connection with his analysis of the intellect as a spatializing activity.[15] Again, Poincaré, in his *Foundations of Science*, explains that "the [mathematical] continuum . . . is only a collection of individuals arranged in a certain order, infinite in number . . . exterior to one another." Provided the number of terms is regarded as infinite there is no

[14] *Logik,* 5 Aufl., Bd. II, S. 48.

[15] Kant, it will be remembered, regarded time, rather than space, as the medium in which number was generated. Thus, for him, temporal diversity, or succession, assumed the place assumed on Bergson's view by spatial diversity. Cf. Bergson, *Time and Free Will,* Chap. II, English translation, p. 8: ". . . we can understand that material objects, being exterior to one another and to ourselves, derive both exteriorities from the homogeneity of a medium which inserts intervals between them and sets off their outlines. . . ."

contradiction in the idea that "the whole is homogeneous with the part." [16]

Now it is obvious that in these remarkably similar pronouncements, by scientists and philosophers of the greatest diversity of outlook and training, there is implicit something of the utmost importance for the logician to consider. These thinkers actually confirm each other in the view that homogeneity and externality—or better, continuity and discreteness—belong, as *complementary formal characteristics*, to all mathematically constituted objects, to the entire content of mathematical science. In the language of Kant and Hegel, these characteristics express the specific manner in which the relation of the universal to the particular obtains in the domain of quantity. In somewhat different terms, the quantitative aspect of phenomena, which it is the business of mathematics to explore and define, is one in which the relation of whole to part is conceived of in a particularly simple manner. Namely, the whole is fundamentally *homogeneous* with the members or parts which compose it—the elements of space, time, and number are again respectively spatial, temporal, and numerical. Also the members are *external*,

[16] Poincaré, *Foundations of Science,* pp. 43, 47. And Joseph, in his *An Introduction to Logic,* 2nd ed., p. 548, says, "Indefinite repetition with no qualitative variety belongs to the nature of space, and also of the numerical series. Any space is divisible into spaces which are smaller, but not otherwise different, and is a portion of a space which is larger, and not otherwise different. This homogeneity or, as we might say, indifference of space. . . . So with the number series. At any point in it there is the same difference between one number and the next; a ratio found in one part of the series can be found in another, and so on; otherwise our x and y and n could not be general symbols."

i.e., relatively indifferent to one another, and to the whole which they compose. That is to say, quantitative elements retain all—or most of—their essential attributes when considered each by themselves, apart from any whole into which they may enter; and conversely, the fact of such elements participating in any whole does not modify their nature to any considerable extent. And the elements may enter into any number of different wholes.

This homogeneity and externality of part and whole which obtains when objects are considered mathematically may be contrasted with the relative diversity or heterogeneity and interpenetration of part and whole when objects are considered more concretely. In the latter case the part is never in any important sense of the same nature as the whole into which it enters, and both part and whole undergo essential modification of nature as a result of any change in the one relatively to the other. Take, as a simple example, the manner in which we usually regard the human organism and its members or parts. Such an organism we may think of as a whole or system of diverse members—arms, head, veins, nerves, lungs, heart—each one of which is essential to the existence of the whole and without which the whole would at least be defective. Also the parts have comparatively little significance when taken by themselves, apart from their participation in the whole—the whole, so to speak, is in every part. A hand ceases to be a hand when cut off from the body to which it naturally belongs.

The contrast, which we have just drawn, between two

types or conceptions of wholes, may ultimately reduce to one of degree,[17] but at all events its importance should be obvious to everybody. It is enough, certainly, to distinguish mathematical explanation from all other forms of explanation, and to warrant our adoption of the old definition of mathematics as the science of quantity. Be it always understood, of course, that this definition does not restrict the business of the mathematician to that of furnishing an answer to the questions, 'how much' or 'how many'—which is perhaps applied mathematics—but that it means, rather, that it is only the most abstract and the simplest relations of things which the mathematician undertakes to explore and develop as fully as possible.[18]

[17] Cf. Latta, *Leibniz,* p. 77: ". . . the space relations of geometry are not merely quantitative as are the relations of number . . . the square upon a line may be represented by the square of a number. But the square of a number n is simply n times n. . . . The square of n is a quantity of n's or a simple series of homogeneous units, which may be interchanged within the series without in any way affecting the result. On the other hand, the relation of a geometrical square to the line upon which it is constructed (i.e., to any one of its sides) is not purely quantitative. The square is not a sum of lengths. It is a figure with special characteristics. The line cannot intelligibly be regarded as its unit. It is its *side,* and as the side of a square it has properties other than those which it would have as a mere line." In this quotation, for reasons which are obvious, "numerical" should be substituted for "quantitative." See also the next note.

[18] In this sense of the word, quantity should not be taken to exclude quality, as some mathematicians and philosophers have understood it. For instance, *Analysis Situs* and Projective Geometry are sometimes referred to as branches of mathematics which contradict the definition of it as the science of quantity, on the ground that qualitative considerations enter into the arguments, in addition to those of mere quantity. But we have maintained all along, that, as the higher category, quantity absorbs, to some extent at least, the significance of the category of quality. E.g., a line

What some philosophers have stigmatized as the doctrine of the abstract universal very probably has its origin in a failure to recognize any other type of wholeness than a quantitative one, i.e., to repeat: a whole of which the parts are quasi-independent or external to one another, as well as homogeneous or of much the same nature with, the whole which they comprise. It is indubitable that this doctrine has a compelling, if wholly unconscious, influence in shaping the philosophical speculations of Bertrand Russell, for example; speculations which issue, consistently enough, when viewed in this light, in a neutral monism and a logical atomism. Indeed, what else could one anticipate from a thinker dominated unconsciously as well as consciously by what we may call the mathematical or quantitative point of view?

Also, the mistaken view that mathematics is a formal science devoid of all experiential content reveals itself as an error naturally arising from a confusion. Explicitly ignoring the fact that externality or indifference and homogeneity are formal characteristics of all quantitative determination of objects, yet implicitly admitting their influence on one's thinking, is bound to result in such a confusion. For what should be attributed to the form of mathematical reasoning in this way gets mixed up with the content. And this is an especially easy mistake to make in the case of this science, precisely because it is easier to realize in the

may be a side of a square or other plane figure, or it may possess other qualities, as the chord of a circle, and so on. See also preceding note.

case of mathematics something true of all science, namely that *qua* scientific, our thinking carries us definitely beyond sense.

So much, then, so far as concerns our first main problem, that of defining the content of mathematics. We have found that the mathematician shares with other natural scientists the content supplied by the world of existential phenomena. But he studies this world only in its quantitative aspects, i.e., only in so far as the objects of that world may be regarded as at the same time more or less completely homogeneous with, and external or indifferent to, one another. And we know now, as logicians and philosophers, what to think of the doctrine that pure mathematics is a completely *a priori* science, constructed by pure thought, functioning apart from all experience. That doctrine turns out to be the product, not of an analysis of actual mathematical conceptions and methods, but of a gratuitous metaphysical hypothesis. This hypothesis, to the effect that thought and experience are separate somewhats, landing us, as it does, in all sorts of impossible dualisms and irresolvable contradictions, so far from being confirmed by any science, is the enemy of all science and of all philosophy. On the contrary, science and philosophy both affirm that thought is a function of experience; that it is a process, an activity, whose main function it is to render experience intelligible. The only valid distinction we can make in this regard is that between different kinds of experience and different levels of intelligibility and reality. And to say that mathematics is the science of quantity is to make just such a distinction.

Perhaps these brief reflections on the results which we have obtained in this part of our study will have prepared us sufficiently for other possible disillusionments and surprises, when we turn, in the next place, to an examination of the mathematical method, so-called.

CHAPTER IV

THE MATHEMATICAL SCIENCES—*Continued*[1]

BY all odds the greater number of those interested in the subject would undoubtedly declare that mathematics is a deductive science. What they would mean by such an assertion, however, would be found, as we shall try to show presently, to vary considerably from man to man. And of course there has always been a fair amount of contrary opinion—certainly more than enough to warrant our raising the question as to whether the majority view is correct. Among mathematicians, for example, there are 'intuitionists' like Kronecker and Brouwer (the latter of whom maintains that "logic is based upon mathematics and not *vice versa*"), to say nothing of other rebels like Poincaré and Weyl. Incidentally, the prestige of these names is enough to dissipate the layman's fond belief that in the sciences all is agreement; that only in philosophy is there no unanimity of opinion. Logicians, too, of the most diverse outlooks and interests, now and again venture to depart from the orthodox belief. Besides Mill, the names of Wundt, Brunschvicg, Johnson, Bosanquet, Hölder, and Hobson represent a minority

[1] Read at the twenty-eighth annual meeting of the American Philosophical Association (Eastern Division), at Philadelphia, December 28, 1928. Reprinted, with slight modifications, from *The Philosophical Review,* Vol. XXXVIII, No. 3 (May, 1929), pp. 232-245.

strong enough to support a real opposition to the most carefully nourished tradition.

In what follows we do not propose to compare or contrast the views of these several authorities—instructive as such a polemical exercise in logic and metaphysics might be. We shall endeavor, instead, to specify four distinct senses in which the term 'deduction' is actually used, and then we shall try to determine for ourselves the nature of mathematical inference.

1. There is, first, the vague sense of the word, which really tends to equate deduction with inference in general. Both in everyday speaking and writing, and in legal, historical and even scientific literature one encounters such phrases as, 'from these facts I deduce the following propositions'; 'from these accurately verified observations X deduced the law of so and so'; 'you cannot make such a deduction from the given premises.' Such loose expressions doubtless serve the immediate purpose of the speaker or writer, and they need not mislead the critical student of logic. Evidently something else must be meant as a precise description of the nature of mathematical reasoning.

2. Secondly, we have the extreme doctrine which identifies pure logic and pure mathematics as the science of deductive reasoning on any subject—and consequently on no definite subject at all—a doctrine of absolute formalism. As we have already seen, certain contemporary mathematicians and logicians ardently support this thesis, and it may be said to be *the* fundamental assumption of what calls itself mathematical logic. Starting with a minimum number of thoroughly

abstract ideas and propositions, whose meaning is supposedly determined or defined by pure thought without reference to experiential data, mathematical logicians have fancied that they could 'deduce' all of pure logic and pure mathematics, according to the very principles or postulates which constitute their premises. Thus, "for example," for certain members of this school of thought, "the notions of implication, alternation, disjunction and negation are formal"—i.e., have no material content—"and of these we may take negation and alternation as understood without definition, while the others can be defined in terms of these two." [2] And in his *Introduction to Mathematical Philosophy* Russell enunciates the five "formal principles of deduction employed in *Principia Mathematica.*" He then goes on to explain that such

> . . . a formal principle of deduction has a double use. . . . It has a use as the premiss of an inference, and a use as establishing the fact that the premiss implies the conclusion. In the schema of an inference we have a proposition "*p*," and a proposition "*p* implies *q*," from which we infer "*q*." Now when we are concerned with the principles of deduction, our apparatus of primitive propositions has to yield both the "*p*" and the "*p* implies *q*" of our inferences. That is to say, our rules of deduction are to be used, not *only* as *rules* but *also* as substantive premises. . . .[3]

On some such basis, now, the mathematical logician imagines he can rear the entire structure of deductive reasoning.

That this is an attractive, a fascinating prospect,

[2] Cf. Johnson, *Logic,* Vol. II, p. 139; Mr. Johnson himself is critical of this procedure.

[3] Russell, *Introduction to Mathematical Philosophy,* p. 150.

even our necessarily sketchy caricature of its nature makes evident. Reasoning reduces to a mechanical game with predetermined and self-perpetuating rules of procedure. Unfortunately, however, a single observation is enough to burst this intellectual bubble. That is to say, it is simply impossible that the establishment and justification of a process of scientific reasoning should be accomplished by means of that very same process itself. Before we can consider the possibility of deductive processes 'from logical principles according to [the same] logical principles,' some independent way of determining the validity of such principles must have been provided. To say that they are arbitrarily assumed or intuitively apprehended is simply and flagrantly to evade a fundamental issue. Obviously a vicious circle must result from the attempt to derive pure mathematics from pure logic by deduction understood in this fashion. And that Russell has forgotten his own argument in this regard only serves to confirm our observation. In speaking of the significance of the so-called principle of induction our authority remarks that "those who are interested in deductive logic naturally enough ignored it, while those who emphasized the scope of induction wished to maintain that all logic is empirical, and therefore could not be expected to realize that induction itself, their own darling, required a logical principle which obviously could not be proved inductively. . . ."[4] In our own words, you cannot prove the principle of induction according to the principle of induction. Here Russell is

[4] *Scientific Method in Philosophy,* pp. 222, 223.

merely applying to a particular case, the general rule, that you cannot argue in a circle, and hence he can hardly blame us for refusing to permit him to ignore the same rule in his own case. At bottom these are the same old difficulties which in an earlier age proved insuperable to those who desired to employ the principle of the syllogism, so-called, as the major premise of syllogistic demonstration. Just as the 'principle' was found to do no work in actual cases of inference, so it would seem that the mathematician must after all determine for himself both the content of his science and his methods of reasoning. It seems safe to assume that no arbitrarily devised ideas and fixed rules of procedure can take the place or execute the purposes of the hard labor of the intellect—either in the field of mathematics or anywhere else.[5]

3. Again, we may mean by the assertion that mathematics is a deductive science simply that no reference is made, in the course of our reasoning—or 'demonstration'—to physical matters of fact, either for purposes of verification of our premises or as data upon which to base our subsequent inferences. In other words, we presumably reach our conclusions by sheer reasoning on 'ideal' (i.e., non-presentative) data. And thus we may contrast mathematics with the physical sciences, which clearly do need perceptual data both

[5] "Mere deductive logic," says Professor Whitehead, "whether you clothe it in mathematical symbols and phraseology, or whether you enlarge its scope into a more general symbolic technique, can never take the place of clear relevant initial concepts of the meaning of your symbols," including words. *Principle of Relativity*, p. 39.

for verification and for elementary material with which to begin. Such, for example, is the view of those who, like Sigwart, maintain that the data of at least the most elementary mathematical inferences are derived from observation of our own mental processes (in so far as these processes follow logical rules).

From this point of view the principal task of the mathematician is to scrutinize previous cases of deductive inference with a view (*a*) to the more and more precise and explicit formulation of all his premises, and (*b*) to rendering his deductions absolutely rigorous and flawless. The ideal goal would have been attained, with regard to (*a*), when it could be shown that every premise was entirely explicit and contained only thoroughly lucid ideas, and that no idea or premise was superfluous or inconsistent with the other ideas or premises. And absolute rigor of deduction would mean a process of reasoning which revealed those consequences, and only those, which followed with internal necessity from such premises, and from them alone. This would be 'pure' mathematics indeed—a body of knowledge characterized by complete certainty and *a priori* conclusiveness. That this third view has much in common with that described in the preceding section (2) will be readily perceived. It differs only in the important respect that it ascribes a definite content to the science of mathematics; for example, the content consisting of the observed operations of our own understanding, or the intuitively apprehended content defined in Hilbert's system of 'metamathematics.' But now, clearly, our discussion threatens to get out of hand; our original subject was the nature of mathematical inference, the form rather than the content of the science. And even if we admit that form and content, method and object of reasoning, are in some sense interdependent, we must learn to distinguish between them, though we may not separate them. Of course you might argue that *since*, or precisely *because*, mathematics is a science with no content other than that supplied *a priori* by our own mental operations, or whatever is intuitively apprehended, it follows at once that its procedure is necessarily deductive. This argument, however, will appeal only to those who have somehow convinced themselves of the validity of its premise—a proposition we have in the preceding chapter produced very good reasons for believing to be false. The science, in fact, we showed to have a very well-defined content, namely the quantitative features of the actual world of perceptual experience. And Professor Whitehead corroborates this view when he asserts that " . . . the leading characteristic of mathematics [is] that it deals with properties and ideas which are applicable to things just because they are things, and apart from any particular feelings, etc." These properties are "the abstract formal properties of things." [6]

4. We come, accordingly, to a new way of raising the issue. So far we have been dealing only with men-of-straw arguments, i.e., with obvious misconceptions, or with a confusion of problems.[7] But we shall be

[6] Whitehead, *An Introduction to Mathematics*, p. 13.

[7] Undoubtedly more confusion is due to the fact that so many logicians carelessly and arbitrarily associate the "problem of

asked if we really propose, after all, seriously to contend that mathematics is anything else or other than a deductive science in some sense now at last to be correctly defined. Surely it is a commonplace, which hardly deserves mention in enlightened circles, that in mathematics there is no problem of inferring from *some* to *all* instances of the occurrence of a certain property or phenomenon. Once granted that the process of mathematical induction, or of reasoning by recurrence, is not induction in the logical sense of the word, what is there genuinely inductive about the science? What is there in mathematics which corresponds to the procedure of the physicist in inferring, from the experiential data that *A*, *B*, *C*, . . . are phenomena which obey a certain law, to the generalization that all such phenomena obey the same law? In mathematics, on the contrary, to demonstrate a property of this circle is *ipso facto* to demonstrate it of all possible circles. Because the circle is not a sense-object but an ideal conception, *the* circle and *all* circles are one and the same, and what is true of the former must be true of the latter. And clearly where there is no induction all inference must take the form of deduction.[8]

Just at this point, however, a sudden doubt assails us. Our friend the physicist objects that unless he is greatly mistaken the law of gravitation (to repeat our earlier example) does not say what we as laymen have

induction" merely with the more particular problem of discovering causal relationships, as worked out by Mill; whence a strong, uncritical tendency on the part of later logicians, simply to identify the more general problem with one particular form of it.

[8] Cf. Joseph, *An Introduction to Logic,* Chapter XXV.

naïvely taken it to mean. It does not say 'all bodies gravitate' and the process by which it was arrived at was not a matter of summation of instances at all. What it does mean is that the material universe is a system of elements interrelated in such a way that each element attracts every other element with a force which is directly proportional to the masses and inversely as the square of the distances involved. The inference (to repeat what we have said before) is not from some to all members of a class, found to possess a common property, but from data regarding the behavior of certain apparently unrelated and quite dissimilar objects or phenomena (such as a falling stone on the surface of the earth, the motion of the moon in its orbit, the tides, the rising of a balloon) to the formulation of a general law which binds these diverse objects or phenomena together in a system.[9]

Now Cassirer gives an illustration, taken from the theory of numbers, of a process of inference which accurately parallels this instance of induction both in result and—significantly enough—in the fact that it lends itself to an interpretation conforming to the traditional empirical conception of the nature of inductive inference.

If we take the series of square numbers as given, then . . . we can establish purely empirically the fact that the differences between the individual members can be represented by

[9] Cf. Hoernlé, *Proceedings International Congress of Philosophy*, 1926, p. 267: "Knowing begins with finding miscellaneous differences simply together. It passes on to find connections between them such that one cannot be without another, or such that given one another must be."

the progressive series of the odd numbers, 1, 3, 5, 7, ... On the basis of this fact, we may expect that when we proceed from the last given member of the series of square numbers, and add the corresponding odd number to this member, that a square number will result; but nothing justifies us in taking this psychological expectation as the same as a logical necessity. No matter how many members have been tested . . . it always remains possible that at a certain point the previously constant type of progress may be broken off. No accumulation of observations regarding particular numbers, no matter how great, could ever enable us to reach a new form of certainty, that would give us more assurance in this regard.

At this point it is convenient to pause for a moment in order to compare the reasoning, so far, with that of the empirical logician, concerning an admittedly inductive inference. "If Hume's account of causation is the last word," says Russell, "we have not only no reason to suppose that the sun will rise to-morrow, but no reason to suppose that five minutes hence we shall still expect it to rise to-morrow." But that we do suppose the sun will rise again is a plain fact, and must be accounted for, according to the same authority, in virtue of the 'principle of induction.' Namely, "if, in a great number of instances, a thing of a certain kind is associated in a certain way with a thing of a certain other kind, it is probable that a thing of the one kind is always similarly associated with a thing of the other kind; . . . " Just as in the case of the sun's rising, so in the case of the number series, all we have, so far, is probability, psychological expectation, not genuine logical necessity. But if this be so, and if induction leads to such results in the one case then it would seem that it was presumably responsible for the same results in the other case; in other words, on the empiricist's own argument mathematical reasoning appears to present an inductive aspect.

But, of course, as Cassirer immediately goes on to say, we do advance from probability to a "new form of certainty," which is to be gained, he maintains,

> . . . when we proceed from the "universal" member of the series, i.e., from its law of construction, rather than from the enumeration of its particular members. The formula $(n+1)^2 - n^2 = 2n + 1$ shows at one stroke, and without the necessity of several tests, the constant and necessary relation, that subsists between the progressions of the square numbers and that of the odd numbers. The totality of square numbers and that of the odd numbers are now taken up into one system, in which the one is known *through* the other, while hitherto, no matter how far we traced their reciprocal correspondence, the two were merely in conjunction.[10]

This, plainly, is analogous to the reasoning in the case of gravitational phenomena, and at once suggests how to deal with Russell's difficulty, in the case of the rising of the sun. Namely, the movements of the sun also belong to a system, between the members of which there exists a 'constant and necessary relation' just as in the case of the members of the number-system. To paraphrase Cassirer's argument, the totality of members of the stellar universe are now taken up into a system, in which the movements of the one are known through the movements of the other, while hitherto, no matter how far we traced a reciprocal correspondence,

[10] Cassirer, *Substance and Function,* p. 262; Russell, *Scientific Method in Philosophy,* pp. 221, 222.

such as the rising of the sun, with a certain other phenomenon, the two phenomena were merely in conjunction. And if we mistake the method and aim (as, for example, of reasoning from 'one' or 'some' to 'all') of inductive inference with regard to physical phenomena, the same mistake would sometimes seem to be equally possible in the domain of mathematics.

The foregoing considerations suggest that we should maintain an open mind as to the nature of mathematical inference, at least until we can examine whatever evidence commends itself as objectively valid. As we have remarked in similar cases before, our appeal must be to the history of the science in question; there is obviously no other material available which will satisfy this criterion. We accordingly invite attention to the following historical details, the accuracy of which any reliable work on the history of science will verify.[11]

One of the problems confronting Egyptian mathematicians was that of fractions and their expression as sums of fractions with the number one as a numerator. For them it was necessary to establish empirically, i.e., in special cases, that $2/3 = 1/2 + 1/6$, or that $2/5 = 1/3 + 1/15$, etc. Only when a sufficient number of such cases had been determined could the general rule governing the necessary operations reach its formulation. Indeed, these early Egyptians never succeeded in solv-

[11] In this connection cf. Poincaré, *Foundations of Science,* p. 386: "... the mathematical facts worthy of being studied are those which, by their analogy with other facts, are capable of leading us to the knowledge of a mathematical law just as experimental facts lead us to the knowledge of a physical law. They are those which reveal to us unsuspected kinships between other facts, long known, but wrongly believed to be strangers to one another."

ing these problems according to any one single rule. Another early problem, of geometry, was the calculation of the area of a quadrilateral plane figure in terms of the lengths of its sides. In the case of a square (of length of side a) it was easy to discover that its area was $a \cdot a$, or a^2. Analogously, it was easy to find that in the case of *any* rectangle of sides a and b, the area was given by the product $a \cdot b$. An attempt to generalize still further, in this particular case, at once illustrates a weakness of analogical reasoning, and confirms the analysis of this procedure as essentially inductive. Namely, the area of an isosceles triangle ought to be $a \cdot b/2$. History also informs us that the ancient geometers first proved the general proposition that the sum of the three angles of a triangle are equal to two right angles independently for each particular kind of triangle, the equilateral, the isosceles, and finally the scalene. And a similar development took place in the case of the Pythagorean theorem.

These simple examples could be multiplied indefinitely, but it may be more imposing to turn for further evidence to more important theoretical constructions of modern times.

Consider, for example, the contributions to the science of mathematics in the seventeenth century, contributions which were largely the work of Kepler, Cavalieri, and Descartes. For the Greeks geometry dealt with various separate and independent types or kinds of figures; mathematics was still more or less at the classificatory stage of its development. Thus a rectilinear figure was sharply distinguished from a curvilinear one. Even the kinds of curves were conceived as each independent of the others; however distant one focus might be from another an ellipse was still an ellipse; and all figures were finite and represented in perception. Now Kepler's introduction of the notion of infinity into the science changed all this. Thus he considered a circle to be composed of an infinite number of triangles, having their common vertex at the center and forming the circumference by their bases. Such a conception can no longer be adequately pictured, but it leads to the representation of it by an infinite numerical series whose sum is finite. This promise of a connection between geometry and algebra was made good by Descartes in his analytical geometry. And finally, for Newton and Leibniz, many geometrical magnitudes are seen to be capable of generation out of one another by the 'principle of continuity.' We explain or understand such separate figures as parabolas, ellipses, circles, etc., by relating them as members within a system, in this case of conic sections, and by deriving them from a common ground or law of generation. History further reveals how out of scattered and very extensive investigations of special differential equations a general theory of such equations gradually evolved. And elliptic functions; the potential function; the functions of Legendre, Laplace and Bessel, all treated under the general term of 'harmonic' functions; Euler's 'gamma' function; Jacobi's 'theta' function; were all treated independently before a general theory of functions was thought of.

These examples are obviously strictly parallel to

developments in the physical sciences which every one recognizes as unquestionably illustrative of the inductive aspect of inference in that domain. It would seem incontestable, therefore, that mathematical reasoning, like other reasoning, when examined objectively, presents features or aspects which can be consistently described only as inductive in nature. The characterization of mathematics as a purely deductive science accordingly reveals itself as the result of an uncritically accepted tradition, coupled with certain 'metaphysical' prepossessions, such as that of the ability of 'pure' thought to generate out of itself, wholly apart from 'experience,' results of real significance. It is now time to pause for a moment in order to consider certain of the more important implications of this conclusion.

It will be recalled that the question as to the truth or falsity of mathematical propositions is for modern students of the subject a very perplexing one. Only one thing seems certain; namely, we can no longer maintain that such propositions are true absolutely. In fact, the view that they are neither true nor false, but 'conventional'—i.e., the logically implied consequences of purely abstract, arbitrary assumptions—appeals to a considerable number of thinkers as a well-established fact. And if it were true that we had to do with a wholly formal and wholly deductive process of reasoning this interpretation could hardly be avoided. But with a recognition of the place of the inductive aspect of inference in mathematics, it is possible to consider another alternative.

With regard to any one proposition we must learn that its truth or falsity can mean only its coherence with other propositions in a theoretical structure, and that such qualities never, in any science, reside in a single proposition taken by itself alone. '$2 + 2 = 4$' is an example of what we sometimes carelessly call a brute fact, on a par with other facts in the various sciences, such as a simple chemical formula. Such statements are true, not absolutely, but only because of the possibility of deducing them from the theoretical principles of the systems to which they respectively belong. In the course of the development of the science of numbers, say, it remains in some sense a fact that '2 and 2 make 4,' but the meaning of the factual proposition alters with each important theoretical advance, as is evidenced by the circumstance that the deduction or proof of the proposition must alter correspondingly. Another easy illustration of the difference induction makes in deduction comes from plane geometry. The proposition that the three angles of a triangle are together equal to two right angles was, as we saw, first proven independently for each type of triangle. And in the case of the isosceles triangle the proof involved the use of the fact of the equality of the opposite sides. But the general proof of the proposition must, of course, disregard such particular characteristics of an isosceles triangle, and must instead be based on the more fundamental properties of any triangle.

And similarly with regard to any one type of geometry; Euclidean geometry was never absolutely true in the sense in which certain philosophers conceived it to be, owing mainly, perhaps, to its seeming stability. Neither is it now correctly interpreted as a merely 'conventional' system of definitions, postulates, and their formal consequences, telling us nothing about the real nature of space. The truth lies between these extremes. The researches of mathematicians and other scientists are simply demonstrating that no one system of geometry can exhaust the richness of content included in the general field of their investigations. Old elements prove capable of entering into new and hitherto unsuspected relationships, and new elements are naturally brought to light in the same process of development. Euclidean geometry, then, as one type of geometry, among others, tells us something, but not all, about space and the possible relations between spatial elements or objects such as points, lines, and figures.

All this goes to show that those thinkers who share Russell's sometime view that induction is only a passing phase of scientific inference, that ideally all science is, or would be, deductive, are misled by their idealism to neglect the progressiveness which is an integral characteristic of all human knowledge.[12] Indeed, even deduction is understood by most thinkers who describe mathematics as a deductive science, as a linear, quasi-

[12] There is a subtle fallacy lurking in the contention that, whatever may have been the case in the past, mathematics, e.g., is *now* to be characterized in such and such a manner. For when is 'now'; and what sort of perspective justifies one in arguing from present apparent characteristics of a subject directly to an assured affirmation of its 'real' nature? And this also leaves out of account real diversity among contemporary views of the subject.

mechanical process of subsumption of the less general under the more general. But this, of course, so far as it holds at all, is of only subordinate significance. Along with the 'some-to-all' theory of the nature of induction we must give up the 'all-to-some' theory of deduction. In mathematics, at least, construction, rather than subsumption, is a principal means by which inference proceeds. A construction permits either the establishment of new relations among elements (of figure or equation) which were to begin with isolated, or the introduction of new elements (e.g., by a process of substitution). As simple illustrations of such constructions one thinks of the line drawn through the vertex and parallel to the base of a triangle, in order to prove that the three angles of a triangle are equal to two right angles, and of the substitutions of new terms in an equation made possible by the law that $(a + b) \cdot c = a \cdot c + b \cdot c$. And even in immediate inference probably, and in the syllogism certainly, similar processes have their place.

Of course, it may be urged that these constructions merely serve the purpose of external aids to fix attention and support a failing memory, thus saving us from incoherence, forgetfulness, and too severe mental effort generally. Figures, graphs, symbols, simplify the notions, facts, and relations in such a manner that the mind, relieved of an infinity of detail, can grasp relationships of greater complexity and comprehensiveness. But while all these things may be true, they fail to bring out what after all is the essential function of the construction. Namely, this function is an expression of the fact that our minds operate throughout by means of ideas, representations, symbols, which derive their meaning from that real world to which they ultimately refer. And thus we are able to account for the genuinely new results obtained by deduction—something which on the view which identifies deduction with subsumption is inexplicable.

This analysis of the general nature of mathematical inference enables us to understand the significance of the point of view represented by the intuitionists—i.e., those who insist that besides the faculty of deductive reasoning an intuitive faculty has a necessary function to perform in the mathematical sciences. Namely, these thinkers are right in maintaining that something besides deduction must be appealed to in order to account for the results which they obtain. But they express their intuitive conviction in the outworn language of a faculty psychology, and hence they fail to grasp the essential unity of the reasoning process in and through all its aspects. Following the line of least resistance, they make a difference of aspect—induction and deduction—into a hard and fast difference of kind—intuition and thought. Surely the example of Kant should have preserved us from such a misguided doctrine!

And finally, our recognition that in mathematics as elsewhere inference possesses this twofold character, accounts for the further fact that in mathematics as elsewhere, history reveals a rhythmic succession of stages of development. Periods of specialization during which particular problems arise and receive their independent and special solutions are regularly followed by periods of unification during which these special problems are shown to depend upon some general principle, underlying, it may be, entire provinces of detailed investigation.

CHAPTER V

THE PHYSICAL SCIENCES

WHAT immediately strikes one as most characteristic of the physical sciences at the present time is the extreme complexity of their subject matter and the remoteness, from common-sense experience, of their fundamental conceptions and theories. And these considerations are balanced, in the minds of the physicists themselves, by a kind of wonder and, one might almost say, intellectual frenzy, before the astounding developments, the remarkable transformations which are daily taking place in this department of natural knowledge. The brilliant successes of the quantum theory and of the theory of relativity—to mention only two of the most outstanding of these new developments—seem not only to oblige us to modify very considerably our inherited conceptions of the nature of matter and of natural processes generally, but also to call for a most careful consideration of the possible further implications, for philosophy, of such decisive intellectual triumphs.

Hence it is only natural that speculatively inclined scientists, as well as the accredited representatives of the various philosophical schools, should feel impelled to formulate a new world view in terms of the latest scientific conceptions. Among others, the names of Whitehead, Russell, Eddington, Weyl, Meyerson, and

Cassirer, readily come to mind in this connection. It is no longer proper to talk of space *and* time but rather only of 'space-time'; for some, 'matter' has lost its continuity and its substantiality, having been effectively dissolved into discrete points or elements of energy, so that the old category of substance—and along with substance causality—must surrender its hold on natural science, while geometry and physics tend to converge; for others, bolder still, the old distinction between 'the external world' and purely 'subjective' experience no longer seems significant, but what is real is a world composed of 'events' analyzable into various aspects or components.

To the impartial spectator, versed in the history of ideas, such a state of affairs relatively to contemporary philosophy seems a natural, an inevitable consequence of scientific progress on so grand a scale. The same phenomenon has occurred again and again in the course of intellectual development. One need cite only the single instance of evolution in illustration of the fact that thinkers tend to appropriate a theory successful in some department of natural knowledge for their own purposes in other fields and even in philosophy itself. At first this is done without regard to any possible limits of validity of the theory in question, even without recognition of the necessity of raising this issue; but as time goes on speculation becomes more critical, and various limitations gradually come to light. In this connection, criticism of the theory from the point of view of the particular science in the service of which it was first formulated, acts as a powerful stimulus. For of course all scientific theories are doomed to go the common way of their predecessors —to be taken up into some more general view of things, or otherwise supplanted, in the slow but certain advance of knowledge.

And we may be certain that the same thing will happen in the present instance also. Such, indeed, is the plain implication of Russell's analysis of the limitations both of the quantum theory and of the theory of relativity.[1] The quantum theory "involves discontinuity, whereas the whole effect of relativity has been to emphasize continuity." ". . . no one has yet succeeded in explaining interference and diffraction by means of light quanta, or in explaining the photoelectric effect without them." On the relativity theory —we are no longer following Russell here—the velocity of light is, in a certain sense, infinite, yet, for an observer on the earth, light has a definite finite velocity. Or, the velocity of light is a new 'Absolute,' supplanting Newton's absolute space and absolute time; subject therefore, it would seem, to analogous objections.

But here, as in the case of mathematics, we must forbear to discuss in detail the various philosophical interpretations of 'the new physics'; on the contrary, the very fact of such conflicting views strongly suggests, among other things, a want of historical and philosophical perspective on the part of their authors. In other words, the one certain conclusion this state of affairs seems to point to is that it is simply futile to join issue in such a combat of ideas without first seek-

[1] *The Analysis of Matter,* concluding chapter, especially pp. 395 *ff.*

ing to formulate, in the light of their historical development, what seem to be the fundamental presuppositions of the physical sciences. Any other mode of procedure, it would seem unnecessary to insist, can only issue in conflicting cosmological theories of a highly hypothetical nature. Such a formulation will accordingly constitute the major objective of the present chapter.

In the preceding chapters we have insisted on the point that for natural science the existential is the real and the real is the existential. That is to say, mathematics, the physical sciences and the biological sciences assume as their common problem the revelation, to human intelligence, of the innermost nature of all that exists. The question, what, if anything, lies beyond the existential, is no concern of thinkers in these fields. This much should be clear, in a general way, from what has gone before. And mathematics, we found, assumes as its part of the common task, the thorough exploration and definition of "the formal properties"—to quote Professor Whitehead—the quantitative aspects of things. Accordingly, we now have to determine what aspects, features, characteristics of the wide domain of the existential come under the purview of the physical sciences. In terms of what special presuppositions and of what particular categories do these sciences construe the phenomena of 'the external world'?

It was Kant who first among modern philosophers consciously set out to supply definite answers to such questions. The "categories of relation"—substance, causality, and reciprocity—represent the well-known result of his study of Newtonian physics, from this point of view. But there are several reasons why Kant's solution seems unacceptable to-day. First, and most obvious, of course, is the fact that according to Einstein's theory of relativity the Newtonian physics represents only a 'special case,' a deduction, under certain special conditions, from the general principle of relativity. And, as we shall see presently, the quantum theory, to say nothing of still more recent developments, has definitely raised the issue as to the universal sovereignty of causal laws. In the second place, Kant failed to recognize a fact which he might have learned from the history of science, namely, that even in so far as certain categories are valid, throughout considerable periods of time, of the realm of physical phenomena, their meaning must change in accordance with each significant advance in the relevant sciences. It becomes our immediate concern, then, to disengage, from the wealth of empirical material in which they are embedded, those general logical principles and ideas which have dominated the historical development of the physical sciences.

In the Ionian philosophy of nature we have the first attempt to deduce the multiplicity of sensuous reality from an immanent principle of being or reality. This principle, at once the source and the reservoir of all things, received the designation of 'substance.' But before the time of Anaximander thinkers were unable to rise above the empirically given material of experience, and hence with them 'substance' meant only some particular perceptual reality—the water of Thales, for example. With Anaximander himself the pure abstraction of material as such, the infinite and indeterminate 'boundless' finally gained expression. The obvious defect of Anaximander's theory resides in the fact that it afforded no real explanation of the manner in which the particular qualities and properties of things derive from their first principle. Accordingly, later thinkers, in their efforts to solve this problem, assigned various qualities to the hypothetically ultimate substance or substances, qualities analogous to those belonging to the sensuous data of experience. These qualities or properties, assigned to the first principles of things as their content, thus became substantial causes, existing for themselves and containing within themselves, or among their number, the activating forces which produced the manifold phenomena of experience.

From this line of thought there developed two distinct types of natural philosophy, the one represented by the name of Aristotle, the other by that of Democritus.

The Aristotelian physics was dominated by the metaphysical concepts of matter and form and development, and by the logical ideal of explanation as classification, of the ordering of the phenomenal world into fixed genera and species. It is the fact of change which primarily demands explanation here, change conceived of either as coming into being, or as passing away, or as alteration. And as all change, according to Aristotle, takes place for the sake of a final cause, which, together with the three other types of cause, the material, the efficient, and the formal, constitute the motive or generating forces underlying any natural process, the resulting explanation was thoroughly teleological in character.

We have no space here, nor is it necessary for our purposes, to go into the details of this philosophy of nature. But we must note one further characteristic of it, a characteristic which dominated the study of natural phenomena all through the Middle Ages and even well on into modern times. Like most earlier thinkers, Aristotle construed certain relative sensuous qualities, such as the hot and the cold, the moist and the dry, as absolute qualities or properties of things. From the combination of these properties arise the four 'elements,' earth, water, air, and fire, the nature of which determine the specific motions they undergo, and consequently the entire plan or order of the cosmos. Thus fire, as the lightest element, naturally seeks the heavens, while earth, as the heaviest, seeks the absolute center of the universe, for the same reason.

Now it is this hypostatization of certain sense qualities, their elevation, to all intents and purposes, to the status of so many independent material substances, which served as a basis for explanatory theories of nature during the ensuing centuries. Not only alchemy but also early modern chemistry and physics were profoundly influenced by this point of view. A certain property or properties, having been determined as common to a class of things, forthwith supplied the foundation for the construction of generic concepts. Thus solids, fluids and gases, regarded as three different types of bodies, distinguished themselves from each other by the possession of certain differential substantial properties, while transition from one state to another (e.g., from fluid to gas) meant, on this view, the taking away of one such quality and the substitution for it of another. To change or transmute mercury into gold would be to take from it the substantial properties or 'elements' upon which its fluidity and volatility depend, and the substitution of other elements for them. "We take from the particular body its particular properties, which are conceived as so many independent substances in it; for example, we separate from tin its creaking, its fusibility, and its softness, in order to make it approach silver, from which it is at first separated by all these properties." Bacon's theory of forms is, indeed, founded on the same general axiom, namely "that what constitutes the generic common element of a group of bodies must be somehow present in them as a separable part. The form of heat exists as a peculiar somewhat, that is present in all warm things, and by its presence calls forth certain effects in them. The task of physics is exhausted in reducing the complex sensuous thing to a bundle of abstract and simple qualities, and explaining it from them." So, again, in early modern chemistry, "every element is at once a bearer and a type of a certain striking property. Thus sulphur is the expression of the combustibility of bodies; salt, the expression of their solubility; while mercury comprehends and expresses the totality of metallic properties. . . . The property of combustibility, which we seem to perceive sensuously in a number of bodies, is transformed by the assumption of phlogiston into a particular substance, that is mixed with bodies; and from this assumption, the whole structure of chemistry before Lavoisier follows with inner necessity." The hypothesis of a special heat-substance, caloric, and of the electric and magnetic fluids, show how slowly this view has been supplanted in modern science.[2] The speculation may even be entertained that the highly difficult conception of an ether, co-extensive with space itself, and permeating all other substances, is the product of a similar quasi-innate tendency to hypostatize certain relations obtaining amongst all natural phenomena.

We may say, then, in sum, that perhaps the most important logical feature of this whole line of reasoning was the tacit presupposition that the sensuous must be explained in terms of the qualitative. And this means, of course, a physics largely without mathematics; as was pointed out above, classification is the logically implied goal of investigation. But even long after classification had given way to more profound logical demands—more profound, so far at least as physical science is concerned—right down to the present time, in fact, exponents of a physics that defines as its task the interpretation of qualitative processes in terms of sensuous qualities have not ceased to make themselves heard. What turned the main stream of thought in another direction, however, was, in part at least, the rôle which mathematics had in the meantime come to play in physical investigations and

[2] Cassirer, *Substance and Function,* pp. 154, 155.

theorizings. But this brings us back again to Democritean atomism.

Atomism began by postulating two principles of nature which Aristotle consistently opposed, namely, empty space and indivisible, indestructible atoms. All change, on this view, consisted in the aggregation and separation of atoms. There was no place here for contingency or teleology; on the contrary, all natural processes are subject to an unconditional necessity. Furthermore, all (qualitative) variety in gross bodies is assumed to result from the (quantitative) variety in the number, size, shape, and spatial arrangement of the component atoms. Such sensations as sweetness, warmth, color, are subjective in origin; only atoms and the void are real.

Atomism, however, was not to play any great part in the domain of natural science until well on into the modern period of experimental investigation. From the time of Galileo, right on down to Einstein and Planck, on the other hand, this mode of thought has had a most important rôle to play, both in physics and in chemistry.

During this period several more or less distinct types of atomism have come to be distinguished from each other. There is, for example, what we may call the original form of the theory, in which the atom's chief properties are impenetrability and indestructibility, and which served as a basis for explanation, both of physical and of chemical phenomena. Secondly, there is the tendency to regard the atom simply as a point, a center of force; in this way, stripped of its materiality, i.e., of even those sensible properties which it possessed for Democritus and Galileo, it becomes the focus of a system of dynamic relations. In exchange for the apparent simplicity and picturability which were among the most attractive features of the earlier form of atomism, this interpretation lends itself to a more thoroughgoing and consistent mathematical treatment, and has proven itself especially useful in certain branches of physics. And finally, there has developed and constantly gained ground the conception of the atom as a very complex structure, a miniature solar system as it were, the elements of which may very possibly in turn reveal themselves as complex in nature. In the exploration of these subatomic regions contemporary physics and chemistry again find themselves united in a common cause, namely, the determination of the materially real, of that which ultimately underlies and serves as the generating principle of all physical and chemical phenomena.

If now we ask ourselves how to account for the triumph of the Democritean over the Aristotelian type of physical theory, the answer is not far to seek. The clue to this answer lies in distinguishing what the two types of theory have in common from that wherein they differ.

They have in common, obviously, the ideal of a unified and systematic picture of the world of physical phenomena. But the Aristotelian physics sought this unity in terms of final causes, of a teleology (which, be it noted, does not necessarily exclude the operation of mechanical causes) derived, no doubt, from consideration of the activity of animate bodies. The particular conceptions, now, according to which natural processes were to be explained, systematized, classified, under the guidance of this basic idea of final cause, were, as we have seen, simply those relatively immediate qualitative characteristics of things which impressed the observer as most pervasive and fundamental. These characteristics were then substantialized, which means, among other things, regarded as belonging to the world of perceptual, existential realities. What is worthy of note, in this connection, is the fact that this was the most natural procedure to follow so long as the distinction between the subjective and the objective aspects of experience remained dormant, or had not risen to the level of a sharp antithesis.

When we turn to atomism, on the other hand, and to modern physics generally, we find that explanation in terms of final causes is ruled out, primarily because such an explanation seems to mean the ascription to objective nature of purely 'subjective,' i.e., human purposes, or the purposes of a Supreme Being. The adoption of either of these alternatives, therefore, suffices to brand the resulting theory as un- or extra-scientific. That is to say, the most important difference between the physics of qualities and what we may call the Democritean physics resides in the clear recognition (whether implicit or explicit it does not matter) by the latter of the independent existence and assumed self-sufficiency of the external world. And intimately bound up with this presupposition is the successful application of mathematics to physical problems. The distinction between primary and secondary qualities is, of course, but an unhappy expression of this general attitude of mind.

It is logically and philosophically important to see just what is involved in this basic presupposition of modern physical science.

Logically, and in the most emphatic manner possible, the condition imposes itself upon the physical sciences, that natural processes, natural phenomena, be explained solely in terms of themselves. This is the real meaning of the physicist's innate antipathy to what he characterizes as "metaphysical" conceptions, i.e., conceptions put forward to explain natural events which are not derived or inferred from the events themselves, but introduced from the outside, and therefore *ex hypothesi* not amenable to scientific scrutiny. Among such metaphysical intrusions he would certainly include both the Aristotelian conception of final causes and the idea of a Supreme First Cause.

But if 'metaphysics' is thus a bugbear to the natural scientist, so also is 'anthropomorphism.' This comes out very clearly in connection with the relativity theory, for not the least of the virtues of that theory, according to its first enthusiastic advocates, resides in the fact that it rids the physical sciences of certain anthropomorphic impurities. Professor Cassirer points out that "in a short sketch in his treatment of the unity of the physical world, Planck has defined the general points of view that account for the continual transformation of physical theories. If the first stage of our physical definitions is marked by the fact that we try to reproduce the content of sensation directly in the concept, all further logical progress consists in removing this dependence more and more. Sensation, as such, contains an anthropomorphic element, in so far as it necessarily involves a relation to a definite sense-organ, thus to a specific physiological structure of the human organism. How this anthropomorphic element is constantly forced into the background, so that it entirely disappears in the ideal plan of physics; of this the history of natural science furnishes a single continuous example."[3] In his recent work, *La déduction relativiste*, Meyerson quotes Eddington, Langevin, Born, and others, to much the same effect.[4] Thus it seems evident that the progress of physical science inevitably carries with it a proportionately clearer and clearer consciousness of the antithetical distinction between the subject and the object of knowledge.

This brings us face to face with the question, what does this state of affairs, which is, so to speak, part and parcel of the immanent logic of modern natural science, signify for philosophy?

Some contemporary thinkers answer this question simply by converting it into a 'problem of knowledge,' which they then rather unsuccessfully endeavor to wrestle with on these new terms. That is to say, the real point at issue, for them, is one of 'epistemology.' How can the mind, the subject, 'know' the object, i.e., that which exists in total independence of the subject and whatever present knowledge the latter may inci-

[3] *Ibid.*, pp. 306, 307.

[4] Meyerson, *La déduction relativiste*, pp. 65-68.

dentally possess? Another group of thinkers attempts to answer the same question by denying the real existence of the antithesis; experience is one, all of a piece, they maintain, and, when properly analyzed, reveals itself either (*a*) as a system of 'events' of which we ourselves with our perceptions, etc., are integral components; or (*b*) as a complex structure of which the ultimate building stones are 'neutral entities.'

Upon examination, however, there appears one fatal logical objection to these and most of the other current attempted resolutions of this antithesis. Namely, such resolutions one and all depend upon a misstatement of the original state of affairs, hence upon a more or less inaccurate formulation of the philosophical problems involved. It is obvious, for example, that the question, "How can my mind, conceived of as an existing somewhat inside my head, as an activity localized there, 'know' or apprehend an object, conceived of as an existing somewhat outside my head, and *ipso facto* outside my mind?" whatever its merits as a curious epistemological point of view may be, is neither implied by, nor a direct restatement of, the original antithesis. Yet it is in terms of some such parody of the original question that most thinkers proceed with the argument.

We need not retrace here the line of reasoning followed in an earlier chapter (Chapter I) bearing on this point. Simply by keeping in mind the considerations educed there, it will be easy to grasp the plain meaning of Planck's assertion. To get at the 'real' nature of the existential thing and of the phenomena associated with it—such is the problem which the scientist sets himself. The solution entails accurate determination of the relationships in which objects and phenomena stand to each other, relationships which find expression in the laws of nature. New laws mean new relations, new interconnections found to obtain where was only apparent diversity before. And the successful formulation of general theories, embracing various sets of laws (e.g., the kinetic theory of gases—from which, as we have seen, Boyle's, Avogadro's, and Gay-Lussac's laws are deduced—unifies and systematizes very complicated networks of empirical relationships. Now if such a development represents a gain in objectivity, in the scientific sense of the word, then subjectivity, 'anthropomorphism,' must mean comparative inability to get beneath and beyond the relatively immediate, disconnected, apparently diverse and disparate qualitative appearances of things, to an apprehension of their underlying substantial interconnections. In other words, to know is to relate, and the more relatedness there is discovered the more objectivity there is realized; such is the simple formula which precisely and adequately sums it all up.

But there is one further minor point which deserves attention here. Namely, what of the relation between the sensory qualities of things, and their physical description or expression? How are we to understand this relationship in the light of the preceding considerations? For example, we see a certain color; but all the physicist tells us is that vibrations of a certain wave length strike the eye. An obliging 'metaphysician' then explains this state of affairs by asserting that the color is subjective and therefore unreal, the vibration objective and therefore real. And if we innocently ask how the two are connected, the answer is forthcoming in terms of a causal theory of perception. The vibration, impinging on the organ of vision, stimulates it and produces a nervous impulse which in turn 'causes' the perception of color. No matter that this explanation really explains nothing; that the formal conception of causality conveniently takes the place of any empirical account of what fills the gap between a purely physical process and a distinctly mental one. Words are so often mistaken for realities that one more instance scarcely shakes our belief in their efficacy!

Of course, a real solution of the problem turns upon constantly keeping in mind the true distinction, as formulated above, between the subjective and objective aspects of experience. In the light of this distinction, the proper statement to make is, surely, that so far as physics is concerned, color can mean only so and so. But the qualification is important. Other sciences, such as physiology and psychology, by the introduction of categories foreign to physical science as such, reveal other characteristics, additional meanings; and, in principle, at least (i.e., in so far as the relevant scientific conceptions in question are sound), these several revelations complement or supplement each other, together exhaust our empirical knowledge on the subject. No epistemological problem can arise here, precisely because no necessity arises for making the metaphysical assumption upon which it depends;

namely, that physical objects and minds are two separate and disparate sets of 'things,' which manifestly cannot be, yet somehow must be, related to each other.

On the other hand the antithesis (between the subject and the object of knowledge) must not be slurred over, for it has a profound philosophical meaning. Only by setting the object in the sharpest possible opposition to itself can the mind determine logically those principles immanent in the domain of existential things as such. And those principles, in turn, can then, and only then, be recognized as also significant, if partial, expressions of the mind's own nature, of intelligibility as such. This doctrine we believe to be strictly empirical, since it asserts that reason is immanent in experience, and can be found nowhere else.

So far we have merely explained the meaning of the fundamental presupposition of modern physical science, the sense in which the subject matter of that science may be said to be 'closed to mind,' independently real, objective. As for the concrete content itself, many thinkers are still inclined to maintain, following Kant, that its general logical—as distinguished from its specific physical—determination receives complete expression by means of the categories of substance and causality. The first two chapters of Meyerson's work, *De l'explication dans les sciences*, are entitled, respectively, "La science exige le concept de chose" and "La science recherche l'explication." "In science these two powerful tendencies, that which postulates, as the substratum of phenomena, a world of ontological realities, and that which seeks out the explanation of these phenomena, combine and interpenetrate each other completely." Moreover, according to the same authority, 'explanation,' in the physical sciences, has heretofore assumed the validity of causality.

What we have called the physics of qualities was plainly dominated by the notion of substance, and the same is true, prior to certain recent developments, at least, of modern physics. And the principle of the uniformity of nature, or scientific determinism, or the universal reign of natural law, are various formulations of the idea of natural causation. Of course, as we have already intimated, the import of these categories has undergone clarification and modification *pari passu* with progress in science itself.

But, as we have already had occasion to remark, certain contemporary scientists and philosophers have gone so far as to maintain that modern physical science has, at one time or another, definitely transcended the bounds set by one or the other of these categories. Thus, for example, assuming that substance can mean, as it once did, only ordinary gross matter, and that electrons, or the ether, or energy, or light, and so on, are not 'matter' in this sense of the word, one might conclude that science has abandoned determinations of its content in terms of substance entirely. Similarly, the various applications of the methods of statistical averages to atomic and subatomic phenomena tempt one to argue that causality, absolute determinism, has no more to do with such phenomena than it has with social affairs: that, e.g., the particles in a gas are as 'free' as are the individuals in a social group—to which statistical considerations are also applicable.

The thoroughgoing manner in which the application of mathematics to the problems of physical science has been carried out, has served, it seems, effectively to make certain of these complications and obscurities proportionately greater. There is a tendency to argue that the physical relation of cause and effect has been replaced by the functional relationship of mathematics, so that, instead of declaring '*A* is the cause of *B*,' we merely point out that one set of changes or events *B* is a function of another set of events *A*. And there is a tendency, rather well-represented in contemporary literature on the philosophy of science, to maintain Planck's dictum, 'whatever can be measured is real,' in the sense that physical science tells us only of certain pointer readings, only that there are interesting quantitative correspondences, coincidences amongst our perceptions, which present themselves as the end-result of experimental investigation. Or again, one may be informed that physics turns out to be merely a branch of geometry; that, in effect, Descartes was right in his contention that geometrical conceptions exhaust the nature of physical reality.

But when all is said and done, however far it may seem possible to pursue these quasi-skeptical lines of reasoning, in the end there can be no question about one thing—if indeed there is to be a science of physics at all. Changes, processes, events do take place, and in a spatio-temporal manifold. To put it in the crude language of the layman, there is something going on amongst things 'out there,' independently of human volition and interference, that demands methodical investigation. Surely, then, occupancy of the space-time manifold, in some sense or other, and not merely the geometrical properties of this manifold, is a characteristic which belongs to the physical phenomenon as such. No doubt one reason for regarding permanence as the distinguishing mark of substance was derived from the tendency to ascribe to substance primarily the abstract properties of space. But it also seemed perfectly clear to the physicists and philosophers of the latter eighteenth and earlier nineteenth centuries (e.g., Kant) that physical change could be interpreted only as variation of spatial relations among unchangeable elements, i.e., elements possessing space-occupying properties of various kinds. The law of the conservation of matter seemed to confirm the definition of substance as that which remained permanent amidst all changes, while the law of the conservation of energy served to complete the scheme by furnishing the theoretical basis for measuring the action, actual or possible, under any given conditions (causality). Such, at all events, was the state of affairs prior to the labors and revelations of Einstein and Planck.

Little wonder, perhaps, in view of the astounding developments which have transpired in the last quarter century or so, that some temporary confusion should result with regard to the logical presuppositions of physical science. But this state of affairs should not blind us permanently to the possibility that such conceptions as substance and causality when properly conceived, may still serve to express, more satisfactorily than any others, certain characteristics and general forms of relationship pervading the domain of physical reality. Ridding our minds of the unfortunate prepossession that these conceptions necessarily have a meaning fixed once and for all—e.g., permanence and efficient action, respectively—we may ask what they could now mean to the contemporary physicist or logician. The unavoidable fact that besides the ordinary properties of the space-time manifold itself there are certain additional properties, capable of quantitative determination in terms of physically defined elements and processes, seems, as we saw, to demand some sort of logical expression. Moreover, the conceptions of a 'field,' gravitational, electromagnetic, or what not, and of elements such as electrons, protons, quanta of energy, and so on, clearly signify occupancy and process in some sense or other. How else this occupancy and process can or could be understood than as causally related changes of and among material of various sorts it is difficult, indeed, to imagine. That is to say, the only way in which the physicist has ever been able to deal with change at all is to conceive of it as displaying itself as a spatio-temporal series of phenomena, of events, regarded as the natural consequences of the interrelations of certain material entities, or substances, possessed of accurately defined physical properties.

There is a chapter in Meyerson's book, *De l'explication dans les sciences,* entitled "The Irrational," which is very suggestive in this connection. He shows how the attempt to express in purely mathematical language, i.e., quantitatively, the process of physical change definitively breaks down at certain points. The notion that among the successive instants or stages in the process of change there obtains a complete mathematical equivalence, so that the antecedent equals the consequent, the cause the effect, and conversely, simply falls to the ground in the face of the facts which find expression in the famous second law of thermodynamics. So, it seems, time does, indeed, in the pregnant phrase of Bergson, 'bite into things.' True, the scientist partially succeeds in reducing this temporal heterogeneity to mathematical homogeneity by the introduction of statistical considerations. Thus the fact of irreversibility in the temporal series is converted into the problem of computing probabilities on the basis of statistical averages. Nevertheless, as Meyerson acutely observes,

> the persistence and the definitive nature of the irrational [i.e., that which resists all efforts at geometrical expression] which is found at the basis of this concept of continuous change appears in a still more striking fashion in a supposition which the kinetic theory necessarily involves, that is, the assumption of an improbable initial state of affairs. In effect, from the moment in which [it is conceived that] things change because they tend to arrange themselves in a manner more and more conformable to a probable distribution, it is entailed that at the beginning of time (whatever we may mean by this expression) they were distributed in a wholly improbable manner.[5]

Such considerations are enough to disabuse one's mind of the supposed adequacy of mathematical lan-

[5] Meyerson, *De l'explication dans les sciences,* Vol. I, p. 210.

guage, i.e., of mathematical categories taken by themselves, to the self-consistent expression of processes of physical change. What more appropriate term than substance could be employed to designate the nature of that which undergoes, or participates in, such processes? True, the conception of events has been suggested as the most satisfactory expression for the becomingness of nature, that spatio-temporal character which, since Einstein, we must attribute to all natural phenomena. And within the event, as one ingredient of it, is located the transient and transitory object, the electron or the quantum. But the fact remains that the advocates of this conception have so far been unable to free their doctrine of inconsistencies and confusions, and that when all is said and done, the fact of existential occupancy of the space-time manifold is perhaps as simply expressed by the idea of substance as in any other possible terminology. On the other hand, there can, of course, be no objection to experimenting with such an idea, as that of an 'event,' for certain metaphysical purposes, provided only that it shows some promise of contributing to the solution of certain vexed problems in that domain.

There is also some inclination, as was intimated above, to regard the 'statistical' laws which apply to entropy phenomena, as marking the breakdown, in at least so far, of the principle of universal determinism, or causality. So the argument runs that two distinct types of laws must now be recognized, the old causal laws and statistical laws. The latter differ from the former in that they merely enable us to compute averages, leaving out of account, relinquishing as practically impossible, the determination of the idiosyncrasies of the individual particles. In other words, the inference is, the movements of such a particle, being unpredictable, are therefore contingent, indeterminate, in some sense capricious.

But this is not all. There is another phenomenon, even more difficult to understand, in the domain of quantum mechanics. What seemingly takes place when an electron passes from one orbit to another, this observed discontinuity of a natural process, from one state of affairs to another, apparently accompanied by no causal explanation, no sufficient reason, stands out as a glaring exception to the orderly progression of events according to ordinary physical laws. Here again physicists seem forced to resort to statistics, to a knowledge of probabilities, as Russell puts it, while Eddington goes even further and formulates what he calls a "principle of indeterminacy," which seems to be the logical outcome of Heisenberg's brilliant speculations on these and kindred phenomena. The gist of this principle, according to Eddington, is that "a particle may have position or it may have velocity but it cannot in any exact sense have both." And he continues: "If we are content with a certain margin of inaccuracy and if we are content with statements that claim no certainty but only high probability, then it is possible to ascribe both position and velocity to a particle. But if we strive after a more accurate specification of position a very remarkable thing happens; the greater accuracy can be attained but it is compensated by a greater inaccuracy in the specification of the velocity. Similarly if the specification of the velocity is made more accurate the position becomes less determinate." [6]

Now it is no part of our present task to impart a knowledge of the physical facts and phenomena of which the above statement is an interpretation. It is in the apparent breakdown of the principle of determinism, of causality, that our immediate interest lies. According to the present view of certain competent physicists, there are some things which happen in nature, exemplified by the strange behavior of Professor Eddington's particles, for which not only can no cause just now be discovered, but for which there literally is no cause. True, there is a good deal of uncertainty about this interpretation of the facts, and no one regards the present state of our knowledge about quanta as more than highly provisional and imperfect. But at all events the idea seems to be suggesting itself that at certain points the causal principle, as expressed in mathematical symbols, and as presupposed in the ordinary operations of measurement, becomes inoperative. In other words, there seems to be something in the nature of things themselves, in the objective

[6] *The Nature of the Physical World,* p. 220. Although the idea that a philosophical theory can receive direct confirmation from science is a pretty big assumption, and a rather dangerous one to put in practice, this principle has already been so used by Mr. Dewey, in his *Quest for Certainty.* The impartial 'spectator of all time and of all existence,' as well as the mythical 'man in the street,' may well be puzzled as to what to make of so many claims, by philosophers of various schools, that one and the same scientific idea confirms their obviously diverse and even conflicting theories. Cf. above, pp. 19-21.

physical order as such, which defies explanation in terms of causality. Of course the idea of objective chance, or contingency, is not new; it is not even modern, for it was embraced both by Aristotle and by Lucretius (to mention only two) among the ancients. But now physical science as distinguished from philosophy apparently lends considerable support to the idea. At all events, the existence of certain phenomena which can be explained only in terms of statistical laws, and the strange vagaries of the quantum must be accepted as they stand. But there still remains the nice question of interpretation, which it is the logician's duty to consider, and which he is or should be in a better position to wrestle with than even the physicist himself.

In the case of statistical laws, for example, so far as they apply to entropy phenomena, and the like, the view that they presuppose indeterminism of natural processes is by no means universally accepted.[7] According to no less an authority than Max Planck, for example, "investigation has shown that if we presuppose the validity of dynamic laws, and therefore of thoroughgoing causality, for each and every one of these small-scale processes (i.e., molecular movements), then the laws of probability [statistical laws] such as have been amply verified by observation, immediately follow."[8] Evidently, therefore, there is so far no necessary conflict between the application of statistical

[7] See note on p. 29, above.

[8] Quoted by H. Bergmann, in *Der Kampf um das Kausalgesetz in der jüngsten Physik,* p. 31.

methods to physical processes and the reign of absolute determinism.

And with regard to quantum phenomena, the actual state of affairs is not quite what such authorities as Eddington would lead us to believe it to be. The real reason why physicists are not able to determine with precision both the position and the velocity of a particle, is the unusual relation between the objects of measurement and the instruments of measurement. The latter are so gross, as compared with the former, that the unit of measure itself exerts an appreciable effect on the object measured, and thus renders any 'objective' determination impossible. As Eddington himself explains: "Suppose that (ideally) an electron is observed under a powerful microscope in order to determine its position with great accuracy. For it to be seen at all it must be illuminated and scatter light to reach the eye. The least it can scatter is one quantum. In scattering this it receives from the light a kick. . . . Thus the condition of our ascertaining the position is that we disturb the electron in an uncalculable way which will prevent our subsequently ascertaining how much momentum it had." [9] But obviously the problem involved here is not that of determinism *versus* indeterminism, but one that concerns the nature of measurement as such. Indeed, the very explanation itself presupposes, as its indispensable basis, a causal relation between the instruments of measure and the phenomena to be measured. And of course the instruments of measure always inter-

[9] Eddington, *op. cit.*, p. 223.

pose themselves, in one way or another, between the observer and the object.

Further consideration of Eddington's argument, displaying as it does such complete confusion of thought on this point, does not seem advisable here.[10] To say that we do not know what will happen in certain particular cases, although we can calculate the average results covering many such cases, by no means justifies the inference that the particular events are not causally determined. What rather can be said is that we do not know the particular causes or conditions, but that nevertheless it is logically permissible, if not necessary, to assume that there are such. Averages mean empirically ascertained uniformities, regularities, and chaos means precisely the opposite. As a matter of fact, then, the only genuine alternative to causality in the domain of physical science seems to be a happening for which no objective ground could be given, like the 'clinamen' of the Epicurean atomists. And so far as this alternative is concerned, all that one can assert is that, actually, scientists have succeeded in their investigations in virtue of their confidence in the validity of the causal principle. Once assume that 'anything may happen,' and there would be little use in further investigation—even for

[10] See A. O. Lovejoy, *The Revolt Against Dualism,* pp. 286 *ff.*, for further criticism of Professor Eddington's views on this point. Then, too, the fact that electrons seem to possess some of the properties of waves and of particles at the same time, and other considerations, are leading physicists to entertain the hypothesis that an electron may be not a simple ultimate, but a complex structure. Obviously the philosopher must be wary of drawing inferences where so many possibilities lie open to the future.

the purpose of verifying this assumption. Thus, in the end, causality, the determination of phenomena in terms of their dependence on, and orderly relation to, other phenomena, external to themselves, seems to be as intimately associated with the nature of physical science as does substance, or the assumption of an existential material, sharply distinguishable from our subjective consciousness.

There remains, of course, the problem of defining more precisely these categories of physical science. But this is a task which each generation must assume for itself, in the light of each important revision of the leading scientific conceptions. Such works as Professor Brunschvicg's *L'expérience humaine et la causalité physique*, Professor Cassirer's *Substance and Function*, and those from the pen of M. Meyerson, contain much valuable material from the point of view of the history of these conceptions, and enable one to estimate more sanely and critically both the rather naïve assertions of those scientists who have failed to keep in mind the logical significance of the history of their own subject and the equally naïve metaphysical speculations of an Eddington or a Lodge.

In the past, logicians have often defined substance and causality in total independence of each other. As we tried briefly to point out above, corresponding in a general way to the stage of progress reached by the natural science of the time, substance has successively been defined in terms of qualities, 'accidents,' 'properties,' 'states,' and so on. As for causality, one cannot do better than refer to Professor Brunschvicg's valuable work, for a detailed account of the various meanings which that conception has undergone in the course of modern thought.

At the present time, on the other hand, those logicians who have tried to follow the trend of modern science are becoming more and more clearly aware that in scientific practice substance and causality are most closely interconnected, and cannot be fruitfully defined in isolation from one another. To cite a single example, Johnson asserts that ". . . the two notions, familiarly known in philosophy as substance and causality, are mutally dependent the one upon the other. No adequate account of causality can be given without reference to the conception of substance, i.e., of an existent continuant . . . ; and on the other hand we can only assign properties to the substance or continuant by defining the modes according to which it is existentially manifested as a *causal* agent or reagent." [11] And in another statement the same writer seems to have in mind particularly contemporary physical science. He says:

It is possible, however, to conceive of a compound entity which continues to preserve its identity through a change of time, although none of the parts, which appear from time to time to constitute the whole, can be said to preserve their several identities. This may conceivably be explained by exhibiting a law or principle in accordance with which the compound continuant develops a changing character by means of the instrumentality of the dynamic interactions amongst the parts or components which from time to time constitute

[11] Johnson, *Logic,* Vol. III, p. 86.

so to speak the substantial material of which the compound continuant is composed. Thus the [causal] law or principle according to which the character of the continuant [i.e., substance] at one time can be exhibited as depending upon its character at another time, may be the ground for asserting continued existential identity, although the material components of this continuant are not themselves continuant.[12]

The point is that permanence and change are now definitely recognized to be correlative aspects of all natural processes, aspects which for contemporary physical science are emphasized by substance and causality respectively, and also that causality gives expression to the element of temporal irreversibility in such processes. This fact of temporal irreversibility is most commonly associated with the second law of thermodynamics, but seems also to be implied by other general laws of nature. Readers will recall, in this connection, the heated discussions which centered around the general theory of relativity, and which finally issued in the clear recognition of the time-variable, as clearly distinguished from the space co-ordinates, according to that theory.

In works on general logic much energy is expended on this conception of causality. Among the vexed problems upon which one is expected to labor are those of the 'plurality of causes,' of 'transeunt' and 'immanent' causality, of mechanical *versus* other types of causation, of the reciprocity of cause and effect, of the relation of 'cause' to 'ground' and of 'cause' to 'condition,' and the causal methods of induction. But the relatively slight significance of these problems justifies

[12] *Ibid.*, p. 82 and *passim*.

our turning them over to those interested in logical and metaphysical detail. All that materially concerns us here, in addition to the foregoing, may be reduced to two further observations.

The first observation is for the purpose of guarding against a rather obvious possible misconception. In the light of our historical outline it becomes very clear that substance and causality are no longer to be sought for amongst perceptual realities, as two among the many things and processes to be found there; they cannot be seen, heard or touched—it were worse than useless to seek after the manner of Hume, for the 'impression' to which the 'idea' of causality corresponds. Rather, we have to do with 'categories,' forms of relationship, completely permeating the world of existential entities as apprehended by the physical sciences.

The second observation is of the nature of a plain but frequently overlooked implication of this way of explaining physical phenomena. Just as inorganic material substances, have, so to speak, no 'insides,' little or no internal organization and no power of self-preservation as over against enveloping media and external forces,[13] so, likewise, the mechanical and dynamic causal processes obtaining among such substances lead away in an infinite regress. That is to say, wherever the causal mode of explanation prevails, "we assume that

[13] Cf. Boiriac, *L'idée de phénomène,* p. 164: "The notion of an individual fact does not correspond to any reality. There is no phenomenon that one may distinguish absolutely from those with which it is produced, as if it constituted an individual, a unity, capable of subsisting by itself, with its own characters, fixed once and for all."

any fact that can be taken as an event in time has its ground in a previous event in time." And this means that "we are constantly driven back to the actual, factual then-and-there collocation. It is so because it was so, and that is why it will be so." [14] In physical science, ". . . we conceive of that which happens as being necessitated *by something else that happens* in accordance with [what is popularly called] a law of nature. In other words the laws of nature *taken alone* do not necessitate any event whatever; we should have rather to say that a law of nature necessitates that the happening of some one thing should necessitate the happening of a certain other thing." [15]

Now in these facts, and in these facts alone, is to be found the sole and sufficient justification for the ascription of 'contingency' to nature (i.e., the 'nature' of the physical sciences). Contingency in the laws of nature does not mean that certain types of physical phenomena, such as those to which statistical laws, so-called, apply, are not, like other types, subject to causal determination. Contingency does mean that *all* causal determination in the last analysis involves acceptance of something merely given. The physicist can render no account of the world which does not require him to exert his natural piety to this extent. Just as for the geometrician space as such is a datum, so for the physical scientist the realm of inorganic matter is, to adopt Meyerson's mode of expression, an 'irrational'; something for the being of which he has no ultimate

[14] Hobhouse, *The Theory of Knowledge*, pp. 464, 466.
[15] Johnson, *op. cit.*, Vol. I, pp. 60, 61.

(metaphysical) explanation to offer.[16] To him, accordingly, it is just a contingent somewhat, merely there; and, as such, it affords him a field for exploration and discovery. Thus, after all, 'objective chance' is real—precisely with respect to those phenomena most completely subject to the dominion of natural law!

In the next chapter we shall see what is the function and significance of inorganic matter with respect to the phenomena of life.

[16] Hence the partial justification of those who used the *a-contingentia-mundi* (or cosmological) argument for the existence of God. They at least recognized the fact that the physical world, taken by itself, is a fragment and incomplete.

CHAPTER VI

THE BIOLOGICAL SCIENCES

SIGNIFICANT as has been the progress in the biological sciences in recent years, there have been no such epoch-making developments as in the case of the physical sciences. The phenomena of life, of things that live and not merely exist, have simply lent themselves to a more and more complete analysis of their complexity and intricate interconnections. But, as we have already had more than one occasion to point out, biological conceptions have, nevertheless, exercised a tremendous influence on speculation in other fields and notably in philosophy. Such terms as stimulus and response, organism and environment, growth and decay, birth and death, life and evolution, are freely employed, with little sense of any call for restrictive or qualifying phrases, by thinkers occupied with the most profound psychological, social, educational, and philosophical problems. Man, they argue, at least by implication, is merely a biological organism, a genus of the animal species, and in all his concerns and relationships subject to the conditions and criteria of life as such.

Adequate criticism of this extensive application of biological categories beyond their original universe of discourse would require a separate volume. On the other hand, the validity of the treatment of mental and social phenomena in these terms certainly ought not to be taken for granted, since grave issues are involved, however the critical question may be decided. Thus our whole educational system bases itself to a considerable extent on the very questionable assumption that the human mind is primarily an 'instrument' to be used for the 'control' of the 'environment,' for the ultimate benefit of the living—human—creature. Obviously the highest category of this way of thinking is life itself; something, by the way, which man shares in common with the other animals and even with plants.

Now one has only to ask if after all life as such is man's dearest possession and his chief glory to realize the serious mistakes, the host of subtle fallacies which must affect our thinking on the most important human concerns, if the answer to this question by any chance should in the end turn out to be negative instead of affirmative. Hence it behooves the philosopher, even when occupied with the comparatively humble task assumed in the present work, at least to sound a solemn note of warning in this connection. When such a definition of religion as that it is a peculiar kind of 'response' of man to his 'environment' is allowed to pass unchallenged, or is enthusiastically approved and applied by certain teachers of the Protestant clergy, it is surely high time to protest not only in the name of clear thinking but also for the sake of the preservation of the highest spiritual values.

From the standpoint of the present work, however, the foregoing is a digression, and, as such, runs the danger of being either too long or not long enough. We turn, accordingly, to our proper business—a study of the logic of the sciences of living things.

Although in practice it may be hard, if not impossible, to draw a precise line between organic and inorganic matter, such definitive criteria as assimilation, growth, sensitivity, and heredity serve, for all theoretical purposes and in principle, to distinguish the living from the non-living. No amount of subtle argumentation can get around the plain fact that these criteria exist and cannot be explained away, however difficult it may be to distinguish them in a few special cases, from more or less analogous appearances in the domain of inorganic phenomena. There still remains the perennial question, however, as to the type of explanation for which scientists should seek in this domain.

At least three schools of thought contend with each other: the mechanists, the teleologists, and the vitalists.[1]

Historically, the struggle between these schools dates from the very beginning of biological studies, and promises to continue, with unabated fury, to the very end of time. In the past, which school has been the most successful and popular has depended, to a considerable extent, upon the relative amount and quality of existing knowledge.

[1] As Meyerson shrewdly observes (*De l'explication,* Chap. II), the very existence of this disagreement emphasizes in the most striking way the fact that "science seeks an explanation," and will not rest content with a mere empirical description, of the phenomena in question.

Thus, for example, at the very beginning of the modern period, Descartes, profoundly impressed by "the astronomical discoveries of Copernicus, Tycho, and Kepler, the mechanics of Galileo, and Harvey's discovery of the circulation of the blood," naturally enough concluded "that mechanical laws could also be applied to the purpose of explaining the phenomena of life in the bodies of man and other animals." Partly because the science of chemistry was at that time in a very rudimentary state, and partly because no one had as yet adequately realized the vast complexity of the phenomena of living things, Descartes very excusably proceeded to build up a purely mechanistic physiology, including no chemical conceptions, and basing everything on "heat, hydraulics, tubes and valves. He believed it possible to account, on these lines, for all the phenomena of organic life in animals and in man." [2]

Then, as soon as certain chemical facts became known, they in turn began to be utilized in the description of the life of the organism. In the next century, the eighteenth, chemistry and physiology soon reached that stage of development summed up in the proverb that a little knowledge is a dangerous thing. That is to say, a smattering of facts was used as a basis for speculation, which, in turn, necessarily vague and hasty as it was, served to fill up the gaps in the knowledge of detail. Even Driesch, in his history of vitalism, emphasizes the fact that with Stahl, one of the most influential thinkers of the time, and a vitalist, "single facts and their explanation hardly come into

[2] Hobson, *The Domain of Natural Science,* pp. 378, 379.

consideration"; "nothing is further removed [from his work] than the spirit of scientific research." [3]

A little later, however, comes Lavoisier, with his analysis of the process of combustion. With Laplace, he "showed that the carbon dioxide produced by an animal is nearly equivalent to the oxygen consumed, and that the amount of heat formed by an animal is nearly equivalent to that formed in the combustion of carbon when an equal quantity of oxygen is consumed in respiration and combustion. He thus made it clear that in the living body, just as in combustion, oxygen combines with carbon and other oxidation products; also that this combustion is the source of animal heat." [4]

Such triumphs in the field of chemistry, like the earlier triumphs in physics, coupled with comparatively little knowledge of specifically biological detail, naturally led to a state of affairs in which "physico-chemical conceptions, without vitalistic hypotheses, became again dominant in physiology; . . . [a state of affairs which] lasted through the nineteenth century, culminating in the writings of Huxley and Max Verworn." [5]

In the meantime, biologists had been busy formulating conceptions referring more specifically to vital phenomena and processes, notably the conception of the cell as the unit of all living structures, and of heredity,

[3] Driesch, *The History and Theory of Vitalism,* pp. 33, 35.

[4] Haldane, *Respiration,* pp. 2, 3.

[5] Hobson, *op. cit.,* p. 380. The same sort of thing could be shown to be true of the relation of physics to mathematics. Just recently, for example, due to the work of Einstein, certain voices have been raised proclaiming that physics is a branch of geometry.

variation, and adaptation, as characteristics of specifically organic activity. Progress such as this, together with a fuller realization of the amazing complexity and distinctive marks of living things, has led certain contemporary scientists to the view that neither the mechanistic nor the vitalistic theory does justice to the facts. The time is ripe, they maintain, for the announcement of a declaration of independence, proclaiming the complete autonomy of the biological sciences, relatively both to the physico-chemical sciences, and to vitalistic, quasi-metaphysical speculations, and for the treatment of vital phenomena in terms of the basic idea of the organism as a whole—what may be called a teleological point of view.

So much, by way of brief outline, of the several leading tendencies in this particular domain of scientific thought. Of course the issues are usually confused by all sorts of extraneous considerations, and all three schools are only too plainly influenced by 'metaphysical,' i.e., extra-scientific, prepossessions and prejudices. A mechanist may contend, for example, that to resort to other than mechanical principles of explanation is equivalent to abandoning the scientific point of view entirely, is to indulge in (bad) metaphysics. This contention is itself, of course, a metaphysical presupposition. And if a mechanist may thus be influenced by extra-scientific considerations the vitalist almost certainly must be. The very idea underlying the various forms of vitalism, which have appeared in the course of the endless controversy, seems to invite such a state of affairs. In other words, the vitalist usually is interested, not merely in the detailed investigation of vital phenomena, but in far broader issues as well—he would base a philosophy, a *Weltanschauung*, on the principle ostensibly formulated to explain these phenomena. As for the teleologists, one of their chief difficulties, in the past, has been to define the 'end,' the 'purpose,' which the activity of the organism according to this view subserves. At all events, there are certain phenomena, they maintain, which cannot be accounted for on mechanical principles; yet sooner or later the mechanist claims that he now has an explanation ready—and so the contest continues, in the form of an endless regress, the one side ever giving way (yet not far enough to lose all), the other side ever gaining ground (yet not far enough to assert a final victory).

To take sides in such a contest were foolhardy, if not presumptuous. There is a certain consideration, however, a certain possibility of escape from this impasse, which seems to be pretty generally overlooked. Critics may attack both vitalism and teleology for introducing principles of explanation from the outside—a procedure which is in itself unscientific—for attempting to explain the knowable in terms of something *ex hypothesi* unknowable, scientifically mysterious and unfathomable. Such, at least, is the usual criticism of Driesch's entelechy and of Bergson's *élan vital;* while the objection to teleology is that as heretofore understood it implies quasi-conscious guidance, or the actual envisagement of an end to be attained. To say nothing of the difficulties latent in the ascription of conscious purpose to lower forms of living things, the idea of an end is very clearly as external as is that of an entelechy. It should not be overlooked, however, in this connection, that mechanism itself might well be criticized as also introducing explanatory principles from the outside.

But other scientists and philosophers have recently suggested that teleology more properly means understanding the parts in relation to the whole; that is, that all sorts of various special vital activities can be empirically determined only in relation to the activities of the organism regarded as a self-enclosed entity. From this point of view, it is pointed out, mechanism and teleology no longer need stand opposed to each other. Rather, the idea should be to push the mechanical investigation as far as possible, quite after the manner of the physical sciences. Just as the way was found whereby mathematical conceptions and methods could be fruitfully applied to specifically physical problems, without in the least implying that the latter thereby lost their specificity, so, analogously, this procedure may still leave room for the application to vital phenomena of the categories and conceptions of the sciences of physics and chemistry, without necessarily implying thereby that these phenomena are themselves merely physical and chemical. Thus all the advantages, so to speak, of the mechanistic theory of life, can be retained, without binding oneself to its obvious limitations and shortcomings. Then, absorbing or taking up into itself the findings and results obtained by this method, comes the application of the conception of the organism as a whole, the teleological method. Here we have, as a working conception, not merely parts externally related as cause and effect—as in the case of a mechanism—but the idea of a whole group of parts possessed of more or less independence and self-sufficiency, as well as of mutual interdependence.

Surely there is no more reason for calling this point of view and procedure unscientific, if it leads to satisfactory results, than there would be in calling physics unscientific because it makes use of conceptions and methods unknown to mathematics. As Professor Haldane puts it, "up to a certain point we can, it is true, understand living organisms mechanically. We can, for instance, weigh and measure them and their parts, and investigate their mechanical and chemical properties." [6] Such facts represent the partial truth of the mechanistic interpretation of vital phenomena. And the mechanistic hypothesis encourages the prosecution of detailed investigations along these lines. But, as the same authority continues, it is also necessary and methodologically justifiable to assume as the fundamental biological reality

> not the separated parts of an organism and its environment, but the whole organism in its actual relation to environment . . . defining the parts and activities in the whole in terms implying their existing relationships to the other parts and activities. We can do this in virtue of the fundamental fact, which is the foundation of biological science, that the structural details, activities, and environment of organisms tend to be maintained. This maintenance is perfectly evident amid all the vicissitudes of a living organism and the constant apparent exchange of material between organism and environ-

[6] Haldane, *op. cit.*, pp. 388, 389.

ment. It is as if an organism always remembered its proper structure and activities; and in reproduction organic "memory" as Hering figuratively called it, is transmitted from generation to generation in a manner for which facts hitherto observed in the inorganic world seem to present no analogy.[7]

Thus the parts, the members, of a living entity—plant or animal—actually contribute to the end of the maintenance and furtherance of the life of the whole, and consequently it is right and necessary to ascribe to such arrangements of parts a morphological unity, as elements in things that have—to a certain degree—concrete individuality. Any organism is such a typical individuality, and at once forces us to introduce the distinctions of inner and outer, of organism and environment, which (*nota bene*) have no place in the domain of inanimate nature. For in the latter domain we have to do only with general attributes, such as gravity, inertia, mass, or what not, which form the basis of all material organization, but which by themselves are not sufficient to give the character of individuality to any fragment, any bit of material in which they find embodiment. Such a bit of material, as a mere example of general laws, consequently knows no inner and outer, has, as we tried to explain in the preceding chapter, no 'insides,' no essential self-relation, and in this important respect differs fundamentally from any living entity.[8]

Such in all too brief outline, is the point of view which seems most reasonable of any of those so far proposed; a point of view which seems to combine the

[7] *Ibid.*, p. 389.
[8] Cf. Bosanquet, *Logic,* Vol. I, pp. 215-221.

methodologically valuable elements in each of the others, while avoiding their apparent one-sidedness. At all events, the very existence of the controversy is exceedingly hard to explain on the assumption that the mechanistic theory is right, for no such controversy exists in the field of the physical sciences themselves. And on the other hand the vitalistic assumption seems useless for scientific purposes by the very fact that it is immediately available to explain anything and everything with equal readiness—by a mere form of words. Philosophers are only too familiar with this pleasant device, so often resorted to in their own perplexities! [9]

When all is said and done, is not the genuinely scientific attitude defined with admirable clarity and insight in the following statement?

> The definition of life is the last, not the first, question for the student of Biology. What we have to do first is to study the actual happenings, the changes, the movements, the activities that go on under our eyes. It is only after we have given careful study to the actual fact of living—which is a process, a dynamic relation—that we can profitably inquire into the particular secret of the agent. By many who have begun at the wrong end—wrong from the point of view of scientific method—the conception of Life, the organism's secret, has to be left as a mystery, or it is mistaken as an entity. By others it is thought of in terms of chemical substances, like the "elixir" or "quintessence" of old, or again in terms of

[9] As Claude Bernard observed, "before they knew the laws of motion of the heavenly bodies astronomers hypothecated powers, sidereal forces, just as the physiologists used to accept the idea of vital forces and powers. Kepler himself admitted the existence of a directing sidereal spirit by whose influence the planets skillfully traced out curves in space without jostling the stars and without disturbing the harmony controlled by the divine geometrician" (*La science expérimentale,* p. 172).

modes of energy, which are "physical" or "vital," to different schools, of materialistic or idealistic leanings respectively, albeit physical rather than biological in either case. Our present point is that before inquiring into the secret of the organism—"Life" in the innermost and organismal sense—we must seek a deeper appreciation of the process of living.[10]

This point of view, correctly referred to as demanded by a proper conception of scientific methodology, is strictly analogous to that of the geometrician, who simply undertakes to investigate the nature, the properties of space, without attempting to define beforehand wherein its reality consists. *That* space, *that* life is, must be taken for granted, else there can be no talk of a science *of* space or *of* life; and *what* space, *what* life is, that is the business of the relevant science or sciences to determine, bit by bit, and step by step—with, however, no prospect of ever definitively terminating the investigation, of completely unfolding nature's secrets.

A little above we observed that in the domain of inorganic phenomena a bit of material, having little or no morphological unity, serves merely as an example of the operation of general laws. Herein lies its entire significance. When, on the other hand, we come to the domain of living things, which, as we saw, do possess morphological unity, are more or less of individualities, general laws cease to obtain in the same sense as before. Of course there are, or appear to be, 'laws of heredity,' and laws applying to various subordinate phenomena, processes, and the like; but of the relations and be-

[10] Thomson and Geddes, *Evolution* (Home University Library), pp. 183, 184.

havior of organisms themselves, one no longer thinks primarily in terms of laws, in the sense in which they apply to physical phenomena.

This striking fact, the tremendous logical and scientific import of which is usually unaccountably overlooked by biologists and philosophers alike, is well brought out by Bergson in his famous work, *Creative Evolution*.[11] As he says,

> The likeness between individuals of the same species has . . . an entirely different meaning, an entirely different origin, to that of the likeness between complex effects obtained by the same composition of the same causes. But in the one case as in the other, there is *likeness,* and consequently possible generalization. . . . Hence our habit of designating by the same word and representing in the same way the existence of *laws* in the domain of inert matter and that of *genera* in the domain of life.

From this habit resulted a confusion of thought, both among the ancients and among the moderns. For the former conceived of all nature as ordered according to (fixed) genera and species, while for the moderns the laws of the physical sciences have become the ideal of all knowledge.

Compare, for example, the Aristotelian theory of the fall of bodies with that of Galileo.

> Aristotle is concerned solely with the concepts "high" and "low," "own proper place," as distinguished from "place occupied," "natural movement" and "forced movement"; the physical law in virtue of which the stone falls expresses for him that the stone regains the "natural place" of all stones, to wit, the earth. The stone, in his view, is not quite stone so long as it is not in its normal place; in falling back into this

[11] Cf. English translation, pp. 224-231.

place it aims at completing itself, like a living being that grows, thus realizing fully the essence of the genus stone. [Thus] the ancients were confined, in fact, to a more or less clumsy interpretation of the physical in terms of the vital.[12]

For modern thought, on the other hand, not only are the movements of falling bodies described in terms of laws capable of exact mathematical formulation, but it is often tacitly assumed that all knowledge must consist of such laws. Thus in both cases the important differences between the concepts of genera and laws have been overlooked.

"The idea of genus corresponds . . . to an objective reality in the domain of life, where it expresses an unquestionable fact, heredity. Indeed there can only be genera where there are individual objects. . . ." A law, on the contrary, is the expression of a relation between things or between facts; and an experience made up of laws means an experience made up of terms related to other terms *ad infinitum.*

The meaning of a law, in the sense just indicated, is well enough understood by everybody. But the meaning of the conception of genera and species, in the biological sense of these words, is not generally so well attended to. A natural kind is no mere artificial classification or assemblage of elements resembling each other only in certain general respects, but a group of individuals possessed of similarities of structure and characteristics which manifest themselves throughout the whole organism. Such a complicated system of characteristics deserves the designation of a morphological

[12] *Op cit.,* pp. 227, 228.

unity. Moreover, not only is the structure thus practically identical in every member or individual organism of the group, but the processes of development and of reproduction—and of metamorphosis, when it occurs—are essentially identical in each individual, generation after generation. That is to say, a natural 'kind' is a biological, as well as a morphological, unity.

But while it is well and even necessary thus to emphasize the individuality of the organism, and the kind of unity manifested by genera and species, as attributes distinctive of the realm of living things, as contrasted with that of inorganic material, there is no reason for forgetting that this individuality and this unity are far from complete, far from being entirely self-enclosed and self-sufficient. The fact of the process of evolution is enough to dissipate any such notion as this. For this and other reasons, which will become evident as we proceed, we must now undertake to fix the meaning of evolution rather carefully.

The general notion of evolution in the vague sense that the present somehow represents the outcome, the development, of the past, is of exceedingly ancient origin. Many of the Greek philosophers, for example, gave crude expression to the idea of the survival of the fittest, while some thinkers conceived of the process of gradual change as controlled by purely mechanical forces acting fortuitously, and other thinkers, notably Aristotle, thought of the process as teleologically controlled. But the vagueness and confusion attaching to the notion of evolution, even as maintained by Aristotle, comes out very clearly in the fact that this same thinker also regarded types as so many fixed realizations of an original formative principle.[13] In all the succeeding centuries, down to the nineteenth, the doctrine of special creation and of fixed types or species dominated most of the thought on the subject of living things. As early as the seventeenth century, however, philosophers began again to entertain the idea of evolution in a general, speculative sense of the word, and applied it, in this sense, not only to the phenomena of life, but to the entire universe as well. So, for example, Leibniz's monads are "full of the past" and "big with the future," and all natural orders of being, on this view, form one continuous chain of progressive development.

But there is a great difference between evolution featuring as part of a metaphysical system, as a theoretical rendition of the nature of experience as a whole, and evolution established as a scientific theory in a special department of investigation. The analogy in the case of atomism is certainly interesting and instructive in this connection. There exists to-day no excuse for regarding atomism as a metaphysical theory as indistinguishable from atomism as a scientific one. The tremendous difference in import of the two *ought to be* clear to every one. And again there is an important difference, though, of course, a lesser one, between evolution as a well-founded scientific hypothesis or theory and evolution as an established scientific fact. Because these differences and distinctions are so often disregarded, even to-day, there exists the danger of a

[13] Cf. H. F. Osborn, *From the Greeks to Darwin.*

corresponding confusion of thought, whenever the term is employed.

In the first sense of the term, and for metaphysical purposes, evolution must refer to the becomingness of all things; must imply that becoming—*Werden*—is the most universal and significant feature of reality itself. This is the sense in which the word occurs in the title of works such as those of Bergson and of Lloyd Morgan. In other words, what these thinkers wish especially to emphasize by the use of the term evolution is that reality as a whole is a genetic process, a dynamic, not a static, affair.

Such a world-view may or may not present itself as a generalization, an application to experience as a whole, of a theory or doctrine found serviceable to explain a certain limited range of phenomena, e.g., specifically vital phenomena. But in any case—and this is surely the fundamental consideration—it is as a metaphysical, not as a scientific theory, that it puts itself forward, and accordingly it is to be accepted or rejected, not because of its immediate scientific value, but solely in the light of the assertion—explicit or implicit—that in addition to, or irrespective of, its claims to scientific validity, it possesses independent claims to philosophical validity as well. And what those claims are it is the business of no one but the metaphysician to establish—if he can. Happily this task is not at present a matter for our concern.

In the second sense of the term—namely, as a scientific theory—or, more strictly, as an hypothesis on the way to becoming a theory—evolution began to figure in the eighteenth century. Prior to that time scientific workers devoted their attention mainly to detailed investigations, especially in anatomy and physiology. It was a period notable for the collection, discovery, and orderly arrangement of particular facts, rather than for the formulation of theories about vital phenomena in general.[14]

Although Buffon, Linnæus, and especially Lamarck anticipated some of Darwin's ideas, the truth is that much pioneer work had yet to be done in embryology, palæontology, comparative anatomy and so on, before a sufficiently broad and diversified factual foundation could be provided, upon which to base a theory in the scientific sense of the word. During the early part of the nineteenth century evolution was accordingly changing its status from that of a highly speculative hypothesis to that of a contested theory. The opposing theory, that of the immutability of the species, together with the doctrine of sudden catastrophes to account for terrestrial and other changes, slowly gave way before the piling up and sifting of evidence in all fields of research. At last, Darwin's vast accumulation of data, obtained by the approved methods of observation and experiment, established evolution, i.e., the transmutation of species, as an incontestable fact. Then the question became, how to account for this fact,

[14] The term evolution was also applied, prior to the eighteenth century, to the opposing and then dominant theory of epigenesis or preformation. Epigenesis meant the generation of living things by development, or unfolding, of preformed germs—a view whose vestigial remains are clearly implicit in Weismann's germ-plasm theory.

and Darwin offered his theory of natural selection as at least part of the answer. Various other theories have been advanced since that time, such as the germ-plasm theory, the mutation theory, and so on, in the attempt to explain more satisfactorily just how the process of evolution takes place, but scientists are as yet undecided as to the relative merits of these theories, so that much remains even yet to be done in this department of investigation.

Now the interests of clear thinking in various departments of knowledge, such as natural science, social theory and philosophy, demand that we learn to distinguish carefully between evolution in the technical, specific sense in which it is used in the biological sciences, and evolution as a rather vague general term to denote the process of change or becoming—*Werden*—in any other field. As Professor Thomson says,

> . . . it seems likely that fallacy will result from using the same word "evolution" for all the processes of becoming that are observable in these diverse fields. We hear of the evolution of the solar system, of chemical elements, the evolution of organisms, of species, of consciousness, of mind, of man, of societary forms, of institutions, of language, of religions, the evolution of evolution theories. Now the use of the same word, especially a semi-technical word, suggests that we have to do throughout with a similar, perhaps a continuous process. But this begs several questions. No matter how convinced we may be as to continuity, we must not assume that the processes that have led to the inorganic domain being what it is are also those which account for the becoming of organisms, or that human history is nothing more than a continuation of organic evolution.[15]

[15] J. A. Thomson, *The System of Animate Nature,* Vol. II, p. 355.

In the biological sciences, evolution specifically and properly refers to the fact of the transmutation of species, to the phylogeny of the race, as distinguished from the ontogeny, the development, of the individual member of the species. Thus we may speak of the development of the chick, and of the evolution of birds. Evolution in this sense of the word presupposes the understanding of three general conceptions, which constantly appear in scientific literature, and figure prominently in theories explanatory of the evolutionary process, those, namely, of organism, function, and environment.

1. An organism, we have already had occasion to point out, is a certain kind of unity, easily distinguishable from a mechanical system or a machine by such characteristics as nutrition, growth, and heredity.

2. The conception of function indicates that use and disuse have their organic consequences, and that—for some biologists—these consequences are at least in part transmissible.

3. The environment, primarily the physical, inorganic milieu, but also embracing other living things, is, of course, of extreme significance in the evolutionary process. "For each kind of organism there is an indispensable minimum of supplies and influences, apart from which it cannot develop and grow, or continue to live. This is the fundamental relation of living things, that of constant and normal environmental dependence." [16] Environment is responsible both for temporary modifications, and for variations inherited

[16] Thomson and Geddes, *op. cit.*, p. 193.

by the offspring. It also acts as a sifting influence in the struggle for existence, against which the living creature more or less successfully reacts, and which it to some extent modifies.

In the light of these terminological explanations we are prepared to contrast the evolution of organisms with inorganic changes on the one hand, and, on the other hand, with such processes as the history of human societies.

The genesis of inorganic material as traced in astronomy, geology, physics, and chemistry, for example, is quite unlike the evolution of organic material. In the first place, there are no material wholes, such as the cell or the organism, which can be regarded as actively self-maintaining, able to some extent to take advantage of alternatives, to register and benefit by past experience, and whose members all contribute to the efficient functioning of the whole. The nearest approach to such unities, in the inorganic realm, are such aggregations as the solar system, or a complicated molecule of substance.

Secondly, organic variation in living things is unlike any process in the inorganic realm. By means of variations and mutations something genuinely new comes into being, while, nevertheless, the forces of heredity preserve continuity with the old. The fact of growth should also be mentioned in this connection, implying, as it does, ability to absorb and transform material from the environment into the living body. The nearest approach to such processes as these in the inorganic are crystallization and radiation phenomena. Lastly, changes in form or phase in an inorganic material are analogous rather to the development of the individual organism than to the evolution of species. The latter implies a succession of generations, whose likeness and differences result from the forces of heredity and variation respectively, and which is totally unlike the result of any inorganic process. And there is no 'environment' in the inorganic; instead there are 'neighborhoods,' 'fields,' perhaps an all-pervasive 'ether.'

The contrast between organic evolution and history, as applied to mankind, social institutions, and so on, is probably much greater than the contrast we have just been indicating. Yet if possible the differences are more often disregarded, and the term evolution is more indiscriminately employed to denote any sort of historical process. In the first place, a conscious human person, rather than a biological organism, is the unit of social processes. Such a unit is motivated in a manner quite distinct from that in which an organism is motivated. Conscious purposes, ethical principles, social ideals, and the like, determine human conduct; in short, self-*realization*, rather than self-*maintenance*, may be said to be the aim and result distinctive of human activity. The 'growth' of the mind is obviously quite different from the growth of the biological organism, while variation and heredity are replaced by much more complex interrelationships and processes. Secondly, social institutions, the nations of the world, and the like, being quite different from a natural species, do not evolve—they undergo all sorts of changes, have a 'history,' due to the operation of forces and agencies largely unlike the forces of heredity and variation, the struggle for existence, and so on. And, lastly, the use of the term 'environment' to define or describe the milieu of the individual, or of some larger social whole, is at least misleading when taken, as it usually is, as more than a metaphor for the reality. To be possessed of intelligence, and hence to be able in more or less adequate fashion to embody and to realize individual and social purposes, and to make conscious use both of inorganic and of organic materials for such ends, is to absorb, to integrate, the 'environment' in a fashion so entirely unlike that effected by the living organism that the very term loses its meaning.

The accomplishments of science, history, art, religion, and philosophy should teach man that his mind, his intelligence, his powers of feeling, willing, and thinking are something more and something other than mere 'instruments,' tools, for the subjugation and control of nature for the sake of mere life as such. When the artist gives expression to an idea, in a block of marble, thus supplying food for the soul, when the scientist succeeds in revealing to all the world another of nature's secrets, when the historian depicts the spirit of an ancient civilization, it is to the culture and development of the mind that they minister, and the effect that they produce is such as to make man feel at home in the world, to create in him that acquiescence of spirit which Spinoza regarded as the true mark of wisdom. The shrill cries of those who have become enslaved to the evolutionary point of view, to the effect that man dwells in the midst of a hostile environment, and the consequent over-emphasis upon the 'practical' value of knowledge are, in point of fact, but the technically informed expression of a perverted anthropomorphism —as we might also learn from Spinoza. And perhaps this is one reason why instrumentalism lends its support to so many unfortunate educational 'reforms,' and why it seems to many critics totally unable to express in an account even worth considering from a philosophical point of view, the meaning of history, of art, or of religion.

This is not, of course, at all to deny the practical value of knowledge, and neither is it to disregard or condone existing evils. But the point does bear emphasizing just now that no genuine reform can be executed, no advance in well-being secured, except in the light of standards of value which are incommensurable with the idea of evolution in any ordinary or valid sense of that word.

And while it is, of course, undeniable that in as far as man is merely a biological organism he is subject to the same conditions and the same fate as other living things, this is no more true than the fact that in so far as he is a merely physical, material thing, he is equally subject to the laws and conditions of the existential, as such. By the use of his intellect he may, indeed, postpone the date of his death, but he cannot avoid death itself, any more than by the use of his intellect he can pull himself up, against the laws of gravity, by his bootstraps. It is only because he is a *human* being, that man can, in a very real sense, through the creation of a world of values, transcend such limitations, and recognize himself as the spectator of all time and of all existence.[17]

In this chapter we have considered briefly the respective merits of mechanism, vitalism, and teleology, as methodological presuppositions for the guidance of the study of living things; then we argued for Bergson's thesis that in the biological sciences the conception of natural kinds dominates the search for laws, somewhat as physical conceptions condition the application of mathematical principles to physical phenomena; and lastly we emphasized the necessity of forming a clear idea of the process of evolution and of its natural limitation to the domain of living, quasi-individual entities.

[17] For further distinctions between evolution and history, see below, pp. 193*ff*.

CHAPTER VII

PSYCHOLOGY AND THE SOCIAL SCIENCES

PSYCHOLOGY and the social sciences, including history, have followed a course which one is tempted to regard as the exemplification of a general law of intellectual achievement. That is to say, in their endeavors to describe, order, and explain empirical phenomena, thinkers in these fields have consciously or unconsciously appropriated and applied both the conceptions and the methods of the other, more advanced, sciences, such as physics, chemistry, and biology. Man a Machine, the Growth of the Mind, Physics and Politics, the Evolution of Society, Morals in Evolution, Instrumental Logic, the Science of Human Behavior, are titles either actual or representative, illustrative of this fact. One naturally calls to mind, in this connection, Bacon's famous classification of fallacies, amongst which the Idols of the Theater, or those errors into which man is led by the spirit of the time, held a prominent place.[1] Of course, it is easier to see the shortcomings, the fallacies of an earlier type of thought, than those of our own age; but, on the other hand, there is no reason to suppose that we of this age have miraculously escaped the common fate of all past ages in this respect. So, while we smile indulgently at the

[1] Cf. Creighton, "Eighteenth and Nineteenth Century Modes of Thought," *The Philosophical Review*, Vol. XXXV, No. 1 (1926), pp. 1-21.

naïveté of the psychologists and social philosophers of the earlier ages, let us also preserve that most important ingredient of a true sense of humor, the ability to laugh a bit at ourselves, at our own intellectual foibles and prepossessions.

In these fields, as in so many others, great insight must be accorded to the Greeks. Plato and Aristotle, for example, formulated conceptions of the structure and functions of the mind and of human society from which we can learn much even to-day. Their ready acknowledgment of the physiological basis of conscious processes, while faulty in detail, is quite in line with contemporary practice. They worked out ingenious and suggestive theories of sense perception and its significance, and both thinkers emphasized, in various ways, the functions of habit, memory and the social milieu in the development of mental life. They recognized the importance of educational psychology and social psychology. And, what is perhaps most important of all, they on the whole successfully resisted the tendency to be led astray by false abstractions such as sensationalism, voluntarism, or what not; insisting, instead, that in general the whole mind is present, so to speak, in all of its parts and activities.

Of the eighteenth century psychological and social theories, on the other hand, the principal significance is historical. In the light of the more recent tendency to apply biological conceptions and principles of explanation to the solution of both psychological and social problems, the prevailing mechanical atomism of the eighteenth century, which inspired the view that society was an aggregate of independent units, led to the search for the units of mental life, and culminated in the 'law' of the association of ideas and the contract theory of the state, seems hopelessly abstract and inadequate.

And that the change in terminology and procedure, marked by the adoption of 'the evolutionary point of view,' was an advance of outstanding importance no one could deny. It has led to many interesting developments and applications, and has given rise to a more concrete and more profound insight into mental and social phenomena. Nevertheless it must be admitted that such phrases as 'the evolution of the state,' 'the social organism,' 'a man's social and physical environment' are, as we tried to make clear in the preceding chapter, no more and no less than relatively apt metaphors which we use at our peril, as well as for convenience and for lack of something better. No doubt hard necessity and lack of anything better *do* justify this borrowed terminology and procedure to a certain extent, and from a practical methodological point of view. What they do not justify, however, is the claim to have established a really autonomous science of psychology by any such essentially temporary expedient. By such means the most that can be accomplished is—as we have seen in the analogous case of the biological sciences relatively to physics and chemistry—the accumulation of data, the raw material of a projected science. And due to the diversity of method and conception employed in their collection, the data themselves must necessarily reflect a like confusion and uncertainty, lend themselves to a variety of interpretations.

Whether psychology—and the like applies, *mutatis mutandis*, to the so-called social sciences—has attained, or can ever attain to the status of an autonomous science depends, then, upon whether it can claim to have succeeded in defining its own subject matter with some degree of precision, and in formulating its own principles and methods of explanation. The amount of space devoted to the consideration of such problems in current psychological literature shows how keenly aware of their significance psychologists themselves are. Nevertheless, there exists so considerable a number of different 'schools' of psychology that psychology as a whole may seem to the outsider to resemble, more than anything else, a chaos of conflicting theories about a variety of subject matters. Closer inspection, from the historical point of view, reveals, however, very noteworthy progress during the past century or so. However questionable much of the contemporary laboratory technique may appear, at least the psychologists of this generation are much more fully aware of the extreme complexity of their problems than were their forefathers. This recognition of the inherent complexity of psychological phenomena signalizes in itself an advance of outstanding importance, and has resulted, for one thing, in the development of a number of important subdivisions of the science—such as abnormal psychology, child psychology, and social psychology.

There is, however, little use as yet in an attempt to thread the mazes of contemporary psychological doctrines, in order to determine what are the ultimate explanatory principles and categories of the science. At best one could only hope more or less accurately to define the points of view and the leading conceptions of certain schools, while it would require a volume of considerable size to discuss in any significant manner the logical issues between these schools. Moreover, there exists an additional difficulty in the way of any such enterprise. Not only have modern psychology and modern philosophy grown up together, but their relationship at the present time—and perhaps inherently—is much more direct, than, say, the relationship between the physical sciences and philosophy. One can be a good physicist—a Planck or a Millikan—without being much of a philosopher, but this seems hardly possible, at the present time, in the case of the psychologist. To ask the comparatively elementary and simple question, 'What is a sensation,' or a 'sense datum,' at once raises quasi-metaphysical issues, as witness the various complicated answers submitted in the past for our approval. One answer presupposed interactionism, another psycho-physical parallelism, another epiphenomenalism, and so on. And many psychologists would to-day regard the question as wrongly formulated. True, whatever view is adopted, it may be regarded merely as a methodological postulate, like the physicist's conception of the external world as existing in complete and happy independence of our subjective apprehension. But there is at least one important difference in this respect between the point of view of the physicist and that of the psychologist. In spite of the efforts of certain meddlesome philosophers—meddlesome in the sense that they seek to inject into physical science issues that can be solved only in philosophy—there is a fair amount of agreement amongst physicists that their problems really do have reference to an external world—in the sense specified above. Psychologists, on the other hand, just as heartily disagree when it comes to formulating an analogous postulate for their science. This disagreement, no doubt, is partly due to the fact, alluded to above, that the slightest consideration of such processes as those of perception immediately raises both psychological and logical problems, so that there is extreme difficulty in making and keeping the proper distinctions. In practice, therefore, most philosophers continue to write their own psychology as they go along, and most psychologists continue to indulge by the way in no small amount of metaphysics.

What most psychologists and many philosophers seem to ignore, in this connection, is the dominating influence exercised by the category of existence over their scientific and philosophical theories. All such outworn theories as interactionism, parallelism, and so on, agreed in the basic assumption that the object of psychological investigation was an existential entity, doubtlessly complex in nature, and participating in various sorts of quasi-physical activities and processes. This may have been the consequence either of a highly questionable metaphysical theory affirming in effect that existence is the supreme category of reality, or of a merely methodological postulate to the effect that the *scientific* treatment of psychological phenomena requires that they be regarded solely as existential in nature. In other words, this second alternative is equivalent to the assertion that psychology is a 'natural' science—for which indeed, as we have already seen, the existential is the real and the real is the existential. And, again, supposing this rather highly plausible alternative adopted, there still remain such vexed problems as that of the proper method of investigation of psychological phenomena (e.g., introspection, observation, or what not), and that of defining the relation of the existential aspect of these phenomena to that which *ex hypothesi* transcends this aspect—whatever that may be. As we have said before, we do not propose to enter into a discussion of these issues here. Enough that all concerned should be as clear as possible as to what the issues are; the science of psychology is quite able and willing to work out its own salvation along the only possible lines of procedure open to it. It must proceed as heretofore with its empirical problems, developing and inventing more concrete conceptions and principles of explanation as it goes along. In the meantime the logician can only offer one or two suggestions—for which no claims to novelty are advanced—which naturally occur to him in the course of his own proper business. The first of these suggestions concerns the problem of formulating a methodological postulate for psychology, while the second concerns rather the relation of psychology to logic and to philosophy in general.

1. However the psychologist may specify the sub-

ject matter of his science—e.g., as the sum total of conscious processes, as the phenomena of mental life, as the sum of mental states, as mind, as consciousness, as human behavior—in the past he too often tended to hypostasize an entity, distinct from the physiological organism with which it is associated, and from all other physical bodies 'outside' of it. Professing to have abandoned long since the conception, so popular in the seventeenth and eighteenth centuries, of a soul or spiritual substance, we even to-day hear a great deal about *the* mind in contexts suggesting that we have to do just with one more substantial entity, hypothetically capable of entering into causal or other relations with ordinary material objects. Thus, for example, the stimulus-response relationship is often regarded as applicable to mental phenomena, whereas of course it properly belongs to the domain of biological phenomena. And so on.

But would it not be more reasonable to conceive of consciousness or mind, for the purposes of a science of psychology, after the analogy of life? This suggestion has an ancient tradition to support it, as well as more or less enthusiastic advocates amongst our contemporaries. Just as life is not to be regarded as a separate entity over and above its material basis, neither ought consciousness to be so regarded. Certain material organizations manifest the properties of life, and accordingly are called living things, subject to biological investigation. So, analogously, certain living things manifest the properties of consciousness, and, accordingly, are subject to psychological investigation.

What these 'properties' are it is of course part of the psychologist's task to determine. Feeling, perception, memory, will, thought—these terms are on everybody's lips and their very familiarity apparently only adds to the difficulty of their study. But, at all events, there seems no necessity, merely in order to be scientific, to conceive of them, relatively to one another, to the biological organism, or to nature as a whole, after the fashion of physical objects and properties, and in terms of physical relationships.

Not only is there no scientific necessity for so doing, there is good logical ground for not doing so. To go no further, there is Occam's razor—entities are not to be multiplied beyond necessity—to be considered. And this presupposition, namely, that psychological phenomena display various unique characteristics, not attributable to organic or material entities as such, yet inseparably connected with certain of these entities, constitutes, in itself, in so far as it succeeds in establishing itself as scientifically valid, a legitimate demand for special methods of investigation, and interpretation in terms of special categories of explanation; but nevertheless in no wise necessitates the postulation of a new kind of existential, or even 'spiritual,' substance. Such problems as those of the nature of perception then take on quite a different complexion, while the interminable argument between interactionists, psychophysical parallelists, and so on, finally terminates with the recognition that it was based on a logically erroneous and scientifically useless assumption.

But to preach is easy, while practice is hard. Fortunately, therefore, the logician can excuse himself, on the basis of a fair division of labor, from putting this suggestion into practice. We may turn, accordingly, to our second point.

2. Our second point, it will be remembered, concerns the relation of logic to psychology. This, of course, is but a special case of the relation of logic to science in general; a subject which we discussed briefly in Chapter I. But there is just as good reason for a special consideration of this kind as existed in the case of mathematics.[2] For one thing, the history of ideas records attempts to base logic directly on psychology, just as it also records attempts to base mathematics immediately on (formal, symbolic) logic. And again, quite independently of this erroneous position, there obtains no small amount of confusion as to the proper provinces of logic and psychology respectively—confusion due in part to the fact, already alluded to, that these provinces immediately conjoin and even to some extent overlap.

This, by the way, is a problem which has caused logicians, in particular, no little concern—witness the amount of space devoted to it in such works on logic as those of Mill, Bradley, and Husserl. Of course, we do not intend to go into all the ramifications of the problem here. Enough for our purposes if we can establish the principles upon which a clear division of labor may be based.

First of all, while psychology is just as much interested in the phenomena of willing, of the emotions, of

[2] For a discussion of the relation of logic to mathematics cf. above, Chapters III and IV, and also the present writer's *The Philosophical Presuppositions of Mathematical Logic.*

feeling, and so forth, as in thought—whatever these distinctions may amount to—logic is interested, at least directly, only in thought. For it is by thinking that we ascertain and establish truth.

But this very fact leads to a second, more difficult distinction. Even in so far as logic and psychology are both interested in thinking, they differ in the point of view from which they study it. Such, at least, is the usual way of stating the distinction. Psychology—so the explication of the distinction continues—is interested in thought-phenomena in particular in so far as they exhibit significant similarities and differences with respect to other mental phenomena; as well as in determining what are the more general relationships that obtain amongst all mental phenomena. It accordingly observes the way in which thought-phenomena actually occur, regardless, so far as its own specific purposes are concerned, of whether or not truth or falsity is the issue on this or that particular occasion. Logic, on the other hand, disregards this phenomenal aspect of thought and centers its attention, instead, on its purposive function—the attainment of truth and the avoidance and eradication of error. Regardless of the natural bodily and mental conditions (and of the problem of their interdependence) which precede and accompany the actual thought processes, the logician is interested in determining the criteria by which he may distinguish thinking—or inference—which issues in knowledge from thinking which does not, and hence also in the nature of knowledge or truth itself—the realized goal of the thought-process.

Now while this distinction may seem clear enough on the face of it, it certainly is not entirely free from difficulties and obscurities. A follower of Mill, for example, might well argue that practically all that we have said so far really sustains his thesis that logic is a branch or subdivision of psychology. A follower of Husserl, on the other hand, might regard all that has gone before as a (perhaps not wholly satisfactory) way of leading up to his thesis that psychological considerations have absolutely no significance for logic—that not only the points of view, but the problems of the two sciences are utterly different.

But the fact which both of these extreme views overlook is that thinking is from first to last a purposive activity, and that consequently the nature of the end which it seeks to realize—truth—cannot, after all, fail to be of interest to the psychologist as well as to the logician. If biology must acknowledge the purposive character of the activity of living things, *a fortiori* psychology must give due consideration to the much more obviously teleological character of mental activity. Hence the possibility, or rather the probability, of much confusion among both psychologists and philosophers; a confusion partly responsible for the advocacy, in some quarters, of a third science, called epistemology, neither psychology nor logic, but somehow partaking of the nature of both.

Now, epistemology, or the theory of knowledge, presumably has to do, among other things, with such problems as those of determining the differentiæ of knowledge, of distinguishing its various degrees and kinds

—e.g., knowledge 'by acquaintance,' knowledge 'about' —and possibly of tracing its genesis.

But the very idea of such a science increases, rather than decreases, the confusion. For this differentiation of various kinds of knowledge, and the epistemological treatment of the problem of the genesis of knowledge, practically always entails psychological doctrines of a highly controversial sort, such as that of a sharp separation of perception from thought, and the analysis of each of these into more ultimate elements—*sensa*, and the like. Indeed, the point of view and the procedure of most of those who claim the name of epistemologist is quasi-psychological from beginning to end. Only theirs is an 'armchair' psychology, i.e., a psychology which starts, not as does a truly empirical psychology, from explicitly formulated scientific premises, but from unavowed metaphysical presuppositions. And upon the basis of the above-mentioned separation between perception and thought logic gets to be construed as a quasi-mathematical, *a priori* science of the forms of pure thought, typified and typified only in 'deductive' (i.e., really subsumptive) reasoning. It is this doctrine, of course, which plays into the hands of speculatively inclined mathematicians, and encourages them in the utterly monstrous belief that they hold an intellectual 'corner' on logic—whereas, as a matter of fact, they tend to be the least logical of all thinkers, especially when dealing with such ultimate issues.

At all events, because of these seemingly ineradicable but hopelessly confused 'metaphysical' postulates, there is exceedingly little hope that 'epistemology' will ever contribute anything to the solution of these difficulties, and accordingly we find ourselves forced to the conclusion that our first conception offers the only reasonable chance for success.

In the first place, we may point out that the question of the genesis of mental processes is, primarily at any rate, a psychological question, and that logicians are interested in it only in so far as the answer tends to throw light on their own questions as to the nature and validity of judgment, inference, and so on. Thus, the psychological account of perception would be of considerable interest to logic from this point of view. It is poor psychology, as well as poor logic, to conceive of thought as externally related to perception, so that the two come to be regarded as not merely distinct but separate. Also the opposition of thinkers like Cook Wilson to non-Euclidean geometry is at least as much a matter of faulty psychology as of faulty logic.[3]

On the other hand, the question of the nature and criteria of truth is primarily a logical one, which is, nevertheless, of interest to psychology in so far as these criteria control mental activities of various sorts. But still we must not forget that it is the activities themselves, and, as such, with regard to which their purposive nature constitutes only one important fact among others, which constitute the distinctively psychological material for theoretical explanation.

Perhaps an example may serve to indicate more clearly the true import of the distinctions we are here endeavoring to formulate. Suppose we ask ourselves,

[3] As for Cook Wilson, see his *Statement and Inference, passim.*

then, what might be the respective attitudes of the physicist, the psychologist, and the logician, towards the theory of relativity.

Clearly the physicist is interested in the theory as a possible new revelation of physical reality, and in the validity of the reasonings, calculations, experiments, proposed methods of verification, and so on, solely in that respect. He must determine what modifications, particular and general, in his view of the world *qua* physical, the theory requires; and, finally, in the light of all of these considerations, he must evaluate this work of genius as a contribution to scientific knowledge.

The chief interest of the psychologist, on the other hand, would lie in quite another direction. His business would consist in observing, or otherwise acquiring information about, certain phenomena, associated in a very special manner with the bodily organism of the physicist—be he Einstein or another—and in specifying these phenomena as perceptual, imaginative, intellectual, or what not, in assigning them as definite as possible a place in the total activity of the subject, and so forth. That these phenomena were definitely determined by a purpose, or purposes, actuating, so to speak, the mind of the physicist throughout, would certainly be one fact that the psychologist would have to bear constantly in mind—but only in relation to his own purposes, not to those of the physicist, as such.

And, finally, the logician would have his own special problems and interests relatively to such a theory. He would be interested in the manner and extent to which this particular theory displayed the characteristics of all scientific theory as such—how and why it represented a contribution to knowledge, by what processes of inference, inductive and deductive, it was connected with previously existing knowledge, and so on.

At certain points, clearly, these three interests would converge or overlap, and would severally or together lead on to more ultimate metaphysical issues. With regard to space-time, for example, the theory of relativity introduces considerations of importance to everybody. The confusing and conflicting popular interpretations of the theory bear only too ample evidence on this point! Not only must the physicist modify his view of the *external* world; but the psychologist must at least reconsider all his doctrines concerning spatial and temporal apprehension; while the logician will be no less interested from the point of view of the problems of redefining the subject matter and the categories of the several sciences involved. And, lastly, the metaphysician will be forced to reconsider what place he is to give to space and time in his general system of things. Incidentally, we may observe that this illustration plainly indicates the extent to which the so-called epistemological problem of determining our relation to the external world is merely methodological rather than ultimate.

Of course, all that we have had to say about psychology needs qualification by the fact that the deliberate application of experimental methods to psychological problems is a very recent innovation, the final outcome of which it were mere folly to predict. At all events the complaints of those 'students of human nature'—novelists, historians, philosophers, and so on—who are always remarking that, as a matter of fact, professional psychologists display or reveal less knowledge of the concrete nature of the human mind than do they themselves, who do not profess to be psychologists, rest upon a complete misunderstanding of the purposes of such a science. The truth in this epistemological paradox depends upon the fact that the psychologist, like every other scientist, must deal in abstractions, and that while he may be as keenly aware as any one else of the knowledge of human nature that is to be acquired by reading good novels, biography, history, and so on, his confidence in the validity and significance of his own assumptions and procedure is in no wise shaken. As a science, psychology does not pretend to reveal the whole nature of a human personality, and, on the other hand the 'study of human nature,' without the control and guidance of psychological principles, may well result in serious misconceptions and misinterpretations. While there is a very real sense, then, in which we may rightly claim that the human mind is more fully revealed in its characteristic products, such as science, art, history, religion, and philosophy, than in any possible consideration of it from a natural scientific point of view, this must not lead us to detract from the very great importance of psychology as one legitimate science among others.

With regard to the so-called social sciences, including history, European scholars are very keenly aware of their intimate connection with philosophy, while

American scholars unfortunately tend to ignore any such connection. What, for example, would the phrase, 'the philosophy of history' mean to the average American student of history? How much insight into relevant philosophical conceptions may one expect of the sociologist? Routine details and practical applications seem to occupy most of the attention and energy of scholars in these fields, while, on the other hand, students of philosophy too often tend to specialize on 'epistemological,' ethical, and 'ontological' problems, evidencing much less ability or desire to attend to the logic of social-political and historical phenomena. Here, then, is a practically virgin field for logical investigation, so far as English-speaking students are concerned, and one in which great service might be rendered both to the several sciences involved and to philosophy.[4] When we think, for example, of the example set in this regard both by Auguste Comte and by John Stuart Mill, who were the outstanding advocates of the science of sociology, we have cause only for chagrin that their bold speculations have not been more adequately followed up and have been, in this respect, so completely neglected. And when we recall that ever since the time of St. Augustine, at all events, continental thinkers have not ceased to reflect on the logical and metaphysical problems of history, we can only admit that we have no legitimate excuse to offer for our astounding indifference towards this interesting

[4] Cf. on the subject of the philosophy of history: Croce, *On History,* and the works of such German writers as Dilthey, Rickert, Windelband, and many others.

and important field of endeavor. Fortunately, indications are not altogether lacking, of a rapid growth of interest in the social sciences and their relations to philosophy. So that in another generation or two we may hope to see this state of affairs considerably improved.

While this is not the place to undertake such a study of the logic of social phenomena, it may not be amiss to mention certain of the differentiæ which distinguish them from natural phenomena. For thereby the contrast between these two distinguishable, if ultimately inseparable, realms of being will be made evident, and this, in turn, will render more complete our notion of the ultimate significance of natural science as a form of knowledge.

In the first place, then, be it noted that any attempt to introduce any kind of order among social facts, institutions, and relations, must involve tracing their history. It were as hopeless to try to understand anything in this domain without reference to its history as it would be to seek to understand the nature of living things without reference to their evolution.

But if history be, in this sense, a basic prerequisite to the comprehension of social phenomena, it behooves the philosopher to formulate an answer to the question, 'What is implied in the notion of the history of anything?' In this connection it will be advantageous to contrast once again an historical process with physical change and with biological evolution.

The ability to formulate laws adequately representing the changes which physical phenomena undergo has inspired the attempt to formulate laws capable of representing the course of historical phenomena.[5] But this is to ignore the fact that mere physical change results in nothing really new; that changes take place only in a universe which by hypothesis is simply there. One side of every physical equation must cancel out with the other side, so that in the end all things remain the same as in the beginning—all that has taken place is a redisposition of elements within a static whole. This is the realm of eternal recurrence.

In the evolutionary process, on the other hand, novelty is everywhere apparent. It does not require any elaborate demonstration by a Bergson to reveal a fact so characteristic of living things. Life means the coming into being and the passing away of generation after generation, of species after species, linked together by the forces of heredity and separated by variations and mutations—always and everywhere the new growing out of the old. It is a continuous, temporal process, extending indefinitely both into the past and into the future. Time is of its essence, and without the distinctions of earlier and later stages it would be unintelligible. To show how the new *grows out of* the old is indeed the problem of evolution. In spite of artificial similarities, there should be no difficulty, then, in distinguishing evolution from mere change.[6]

[5] E.g., by Buckle, *et al.* Cf. Croce, *On History,* pp. 297 *ff.*

[6] In a paper read before the International Congress of Philosophy at Oxford University, entitled "Cosmic Progress and Living Activity," Professor H. Wildon Carr distinguishes between physical change and vital processes in the following terms: "One difference between them is the different way in which time enters into the conception of each. Both kinds of process imply succession, both

But that history differs even more from evolution than does the latter from physical change, is not so readily appreciated. For this reason we must emphasize the distinctions a little more fully.

Organic evolution is a natural process. It takes place or occurs. The elements which are involved in it are all taken from the material environment, and to this environment they inevitably return again. A single purpose is everywhere present in the process, as in the nest-building of birds; the blind, indiscriminate, ruthless purpose, namely, of life itself. This purpose has to contend against the perfectly neutral and indifferent forces of the material environment, against itself as manifested in divers units, and against the conscious will of man. And from the evolutionary point of view good and bad are purely relative terms.

History is not a natural process, and cannot be understood as such. Historical events cannot be presented to, or grasped by, the senses, as can purely natural events—they cannot be pictured, in other words. The student of natural phenomena holds him-

imply the time-dimension with its indivisible forward direction, but the reality of time means something different in each concept. For quantitative process or movement time is a series of moments each of which in determining its successor has ceased to exist. The present moment alone exists and all existence belongs to it, the past moments have been but are not, the future are not but will be; and this present moment itself has no duration and is not a dimension, it is a dividing line between past and future. In physics the world is conceived as such a process. . . . On the other hand, in qualitative process . . . time endures. Duration is a continuity of existence, not a continual passing out of existence. The past never ceases to exist, and the present is cumulative." Although there is some confusion here, the general idea is the same as in the text.

self towards them as a spectator; the historian, on the other hand, must in some sense live himself into the past in order to understand it. History is not simply there to be found out by observation and experiment; it has, as we say, to be 'made.' This tremendously important fact means that it can be comprehended only in terms of ideas, meanings, purposes. We may perhaps explain all of the external conditions of historical events according to the principles of the natural sciences, but after all it is only in terms of ideas that the Middle Ages, the French Revolution, Christianity, can be understood historically. And ideas are not natural occurrences, but products, creations, of the human mind. Hence it is only in the medium of mind that history has any reality. Hegel was the first to realize this fact, but even he failed to grasp it in all its fullness.

For evolution the past is gone irretrievably; each period of the past is a stage leading on to what immediately follows. The present is the outgrowth of the past and the basis of what is to follow. For history, on the other hand, all of the past, and not merely the preceding stage, is always there to be understood, appropriated, and used. As Croce so well says, all history is in this sense contemporary. And this means that each new generation must first take up the past into its own experience by its own efforts—there is no passive inheritance, as in organic nature, of what has gone before, no endowment not acquired by mental labor. As a reward for this labor, all of the past serves as material to be freely drawn upon for the realization of present ideas and future purposes.[7] And our attitude towards this past may be positive, negative, or a mixture of both.

History, then, is not continuous in the same sense as is evolution. This may be seen, too, when we consider the future instead of the past. For the idea of progress, seemingly so essential to historical understanding, involves the determination of criteria which can be applied to the future as well as to the past. From the historical point of view, good and bad are not merely relative terms, but are in some sense absolute and eternal.

Perhaps enough has been said, sufficiently to distinguish, for our present purposes, evolution from history, natural phenomena from social phenomena. It is only in the light of such distinctions, we would urge, that the logic of the social sciences can be worked out. But that, clearly, is a task for another time.

[7] This is the practical significance of history.

CHAPTER VIII

CONCLUSION: SOME METAPHYSICAL OBSERVATIONS

IN the preceding chapters we have been engaged in defining the content, method, and primary aims of those among the natural sciences which have exerted the greatest influence on philosophical speculation.

To this end we have found it necessary, time and again, to expose what we may call a fallacy of idealization. This very common fallacy arises from the fact that science, like every other human enterprise, calls for philosophical interpretation and evaluation. Recognition of this fact, especially if unconscious, together with intellectual absorption, either in one science in particular, or in science in general, to the consequent neglect of the many other equally legitimate motives for philosophizing, leads almost inevitably to such idealization.

That it is possible thus to idealize not only mathematics but also both the physical sciences and the biological sciences, both history and contemporary thought bear only too ample witness. Hence, at any rate, the disease contains within itself the germs which should in time effect its own cure! For one idealization opposes itself at every point to each of the others, in such a way that a normal, healthy intelligence, not diseased to begin with, may soon learn how to avoid becoming infected with an otherwise possibly insidious doctrine.

And the same is true, *mutatis mutandis,* of science in general. To oppose the idea of the validity of the scientific method in philosophy, advocates of æsthetics, or history, or what not, as the organon of philosophy, will and do most assuredly make themselves heard. Perhaps, in the long run—and with such unintentional assistance as this—philosophy may get a chance to proclaim its own rights, to specific methods and problems of its own!

At all events, when, and only when, these self-destructive idealizations shall have been induced to confront, and so to cancel each other, will it become possible to carry out a really logical examination of the several natural sciences. How far we have succeeded in this task is another question, but at all events we may safely claim that this sort of critical endeavor is both interesting on its own account and important for culture in general. And perhaps it will not be amiss, in this connection, briefly to summarize the main points which have emerged from our study.

Natural science, we found, assumes as its peculiar province the exploration of the existential aspects of our experience. It seeks to understand, to describe or explain, the properties and relations of things *qua* things. Even psychology, when conceived of as an 'empirical' science, perforce and likewise restricts itself to an investigation of the existential aspects of mental phenomena.

In mathematics we have to do only with those most elementary and abstract properties and relations of things which find expression in the definition of the science as the science of quantity—space, time, and number—or, in Mr. Whitehead's characterization, as the science which studies the "formal properties" of things. Of course, it must not be forgotten that our experience of sense qualities, in perception, serves as the basis of all scientific endeavor, and that this qualitative aspect of things is in varying degrees of completeness assimilated in and through the higher categories of the several natural sciences. And this assimilation is effected largely through the process of measurement, which thus functions as the connecting link between mathematics and the other sciences, and which is only a higher, i.e., more precise and complete form of that double-sided process of comparison and discrimination which begins on the qualitative level of experience.[1]

If this characterization be found unsatisfactory and absurdly narrow and antiquated by those mathematicians and philosophers who are bent, with a true religious frenzy, on idealizing the science, even to the extent of raising it, by the brute force of abstract reasoning, above and beyond this hurly-burly world of actual experience, to the sublime heights of intellectual legerdemain with meaningless symbols, other mathematicians and philosophers may find consolation in the reflection that to stick to reality is in itself no mean ideal, and that the most glorious names in the history of mathematics belong to those who knew how to develop their science by natural rather than supernatural con-

[1] Cf. on the important subject of measurement, so far as it relates to the mathematical sciences,. Spaier, *La pensée et la quantité;* Bosanquet, *Logic,* Vol. I; Russell, *The Principles of Mathematics.*

siderations. And if it appear glorious to some to 'deduce' a chain of tautologies, one from the other, after the model, 'if *p*, then *p;* but *p*, therefore *p*,' to others it will seem more significant to follow the sure march of a natural science, making use only of the well-attested principles of scientific inference as such, and achieving those results which history acquaints us with. In one sense only, then, is mathematical knowledge the light, and the mathematical method the way, to all true knowledge—in the sense, namely, that the general nature of scientific inference is more clearly because more simply—and therefore not quite adequately—exemplified in mathematics, than in the other natural sciences.

In this order of ideas, the following pregnant remarks of Brunschvicg most clearly and forcibly illustrate our position:

The circle within which mathematical studies appeared to be enclosed at the beginning of the XIXth century has been broken through at all points. Algebra with Galois, analysis with Cauchy, geometry with Lobatchewski . . . have opened new paths for themselves; and the conception of the relation, in mathematics, between principles assumed and consequences inferred, has been radically modified; while syllogistic or logistic deduction excludes everything unforeseen from the conclusion, it is precisely within the region where the mathematician seems to have bestowed upon himself, by mere voluntary caprice, objects most remote from sense experience, that some of the greatest surprises in the search for truth have appeared. From the consideration of a property like convergence or divergence there is going to result a radical difference between series, which both by the nature of their terms, and by their formal constitution, seemed practically identical; elsewhere, on the other hand, there are going to appear analogies which no prevision could have anticipated.[2]

Here we have elucidated, in no uncertain fashion, the manner in which scientific knowledge develops, and the inseparability of the two aspects—deduction and induction—of all scientific inference. And as Brunschvicg further acutely observes, pursuing the same argument, and indicating, incidentally, the close touch of mathematics with experience, physical science has played no small rôle in this prodigious development. As a single example, we note that "in order to resolve the problems to which the equational expression of experimental results concerning radiant heat naturally led, Fourier undertook the systematic study of discontinuous functions not developable in Talorian series, and thus enriched analysis with an almost completely new domain." [3]

For this conception of the experiential subject matter, methods, and aims of the mathematical sciences we have argued at some length, basing our contentions entirely upon an empirical, historical reflection upon the sciences in question, and as far as possible without reference to any special ulterior metaphysical implications. With regard to the physical sciences—physics, chemistry, etc.—that is to say, respecting those sciences which investigate the more concrete properties and relations of material substances, our aim was likewise to discover what categories and principles of explanation have emerged in the course of their long history. In

[2] Brunschvicg, *L'expérience humaine et la causalité physique*, p. 601.

[3] *Ibid.*, p. 602.

this domain we have found that it still seems true that, "the conception of the world which [physical] science presents to us is the conception of a multiplicity of substances, acting and reacting on each other, and by their action producing continual changes in each other according to unchanging laws." [4]

In a sense, then, it would seem as if we might say that the conception or category of substance bridges the gap between the categories of quality and quantity on the one hand, and that of causality on the other. The conception of (unchanging) substance as possessing (changing) attributes seems on this view more akin to the former categories, while the conception of substance as itself changing, as "a dynamic energy which from its very nature is in perpetual necessitated change," [5] is more akin to the latter.

We furthermore argued that causality has meaning only with reference to the contingent, to that which must be accepted as merely and—so far—unaccountably given. And, in passing, we may point out that this characteristic of inexplicable givenness—offering,

[4] Caird, *Hegel,* p. 173. Cf. also Caird, *Kant,* Vol. I, p. 516: ". . . we have a kind of synthetic unity established by the mathematical principles. But 'it is a synthesis of the homogeneous, and so of elements which do not necessarily belong to, or require each other, as, e.g., the two triangles into which a quadrilateral is divided by the diagonal do not when taken severally, require each other.' But the dynamical synthesis 'is the synthesis of the manifold in so far as its elements necessarily belong to each other, as, e.g., the accident to some particular substance, or the effect to its cause; a synthesis in which different elements are represented as heterogeneous and yet as united together *a priori.*' Such a synthesis is not arbitrary (like the other) for it is 'a connection which concerns the existence of the manifold.'"

[5] The phrase is Professor Kemp Smith's (*Commentary to Kant,* p. 362).

as it does, such ample scope for natural piety—applies, and applies only, to that obviously abstract fragment of experience, the universe *qua* physical. It is no accident, therefore, but a logical consequence of this fact, that those who insist on a datum, on a level of experience which tradition calls 'immediate,' as a presupposition of their philosophy, should never be able to transcend in their thought the point of view of the existential. To idealize existence, to identify in this fashion physical existence with reality, is indeed a far too common habit of the self-styled realistic and empirically minded philosophers. This means, of course, that the resulting philosophy can never rise above—though it may well fall below—the opposition or dualism of the subject and the object of knowledge, for the former must be conceived of in terms of the latter, i.e., as one existential, and therefore external, object among others.[6]

As a matter of fact, however, the biological sciences themselves, to say nothing of a critical philosophy, carry us beyond this point of view. For in the language of biology two distinct types of objects find recognition, indicated respectively by the terms 'organism' and 'environment.' The new kind of facts, represented by this change in terminology, seem, as we have shown, to demand interpretation and explanation in terms of new categories, such as purposiveness, in addition to those underlying the more abstract sciences. At all events the evolutionary process of change, entailing, as it does,

[6] The reply to this type of philosophy is, as Brunschvicg somewhere observes, that man is indeed only a body *among bodies,* and that he first becomes a man *among men.*

both conflict and coöperation between the one kind of object and the other, calls for a form of explanation which, we have maintained, differs in important respects from that obtaining in the physical sciences. This difference is most plainly marked by the all-important conception and method of genetic classification, which recognizes the existence of natural kinds, gradually undergoing modification in the course of time—a type of change for which there is no parallel in the realm of the merely physical. Accordingly, we follow Bergson in the view that in the biological sciences causal laws, instead of occupying the central rôle rightly assigned to them in the physical sciences, have a strictly subordinate, though nevertheless important, part to play.

On this level of animal existence the intellect, i.e., human intelligence, naturally comes to be thought of as a tool or instrument, serving man—an animal as much as any other—in his struggles with the environment. Consequently, an idealization of the biological point of view will emphasize this conception by declaring that in reality thought is a problem-solving activity, directed to the prediction and control of the future course of environmental phenomena to the end of the safeguarding and furtherance of desirable consequences. The appeal of this 'philosophy of life' is eminently insidious in the case of a people occupied primarily with the conquest of nature and the exploitation of the material goods of life, for it seems to confirm the everlasting significance of their commonplace daily experiences, and to offer the support and encouragement of philosophy to their mundane enterprises. But we have already had occasion to criticize the application of the idea of evolution to human institutions, and of the significance of science, art, religion, and other characteristically human interests, this philosophy is unable to speak, except in terms which degrade them to the level of barely 'practical' implements.

One may point out, in passing, also, that while thought is, among other things, a problem-solving activity, it is also, and perhaps more characteristically, a problem-raising activity. 'More characteristically,' because the ability thus to raise problems, to ask *disinterested* questions concerning the ultimate nature of things, and so on, is one of the distinguishing marks of mankind as such. And to over-emphasize the practical consequences of our thinking is just to fail to grasp this important truth. There is a sense, however, as we shall see presently, in which it is most important not to disregard the practical value of science.

Our study of the logic of psychology and of the social sciences limited itself to a few observations, the main purpose of which was to indicate the pressing need of a thorough logical examination of these sciences, and especially of sociology and history. We can only express the hope that in due course of time these problems will receive the attention they deserve from English-speaking students. But that the social sciences, especially, do reveal new attributes and capacities of mind, unrecognized so long as we confine ourselves to the point of view of natural knowledge—that is a fact which we have endeavored to insist upon as forcibly as possible.

This brings us to another phase of our subject, and one in which we can hardly avoid raising explicitly metaphysical issues.

There is a common doctrine to the effect that at least part of the business of philosophy consists in reconciling and synthesizing the points of view and the findings of the several sciences, and that in this way scientific knowledge may be said to contribute to our philosophical understanding of the world. But the fact is, that neither scientists nor philosophers, with some few exceptions, ever get beyond the bare assertion. Usually, the execution of the program is left to other hands, on the plea of insufficient knowledge, either of philosophy or of science, as the case may be. But the time has come when one may well raise the question, whether it is not intellectually immoral thus to evade the issue. For an honest effort to work out this excellent program would scarcely leave unmodified the sum total of one's philosophical convictions. Hence one of our aims, in the present study, is to contribute something to the actual realization of this synthesis.

Clearly this task cannot be accomplished merely by the appropriation of the scientific method, so called,[7] and neither can it be completed without a due evaluation of the social sciences as well as of the natural sciences. Most important of all, however, any such endeavor must duly acknowledge the fundamental principle that knowledge involves both a subject and an object. However 'independent' objects may be so far as their existence is concerned—and that natural

[7] Cf. above, p. 18.

science rightly assumes the independent existence of its objects we have argued throughout—when not merely the properties and relations of objects *qua* existences are at stake, but when the question as to the characteristics of natural knowledge itself is raised, failure to acknowledge this principle is fatal. In other words—to repeat once again a central theme of this work—the critical examination of knowledge, with a view to formulating the logical principles which it entails, reveals *pari passu* as much about the mind which knows as it does about the object known. If we say, for example, that mathematics considers objects from the quantitative point of view, we are also saying that quantity is one of the categories of knowledge, one of the ways in which the mind finds a satisfaction of its natural desire to know. Quantity is thus a form of scientific intelligibility, as such, or, as we may say indifferently, of the mind which knows. Such, then, is the basic presupposition of any valid synthesis of the sciences, from the philosophical point of view.

In the light of this principle one comes to distinguish higher and lower levels of intelligibility. For example, the quantitative determination of objects, is, as we have seen, 'external,' i.e., objects quantitatively considered *ipso facto* have no essential connection with one another, constitute no actual whole; and hence the most heterogeneous objects are subject to such determination. We have only to establish any simple criterion by which to distinguish one thing from another in order to count, measure and compute. Other quantitative determinations—such as spatial, or spatio-temporal—

may be more complex and the relationships accordingly not quite so external, but this does not alter the essential fact about the great abstractness of such determinations. But to speak of one object, phenomenon, or event, as cause of another, or to talk of the universal reign of causal laws, is to assert not merely that things are together and that they may be compared and distinguished as to number, position, and the like, but that they in some measure actually belong together. However 'external' the terms of the causal relationship may be—*causa sui* is apparently a contradiction in terms—there must still be some identity of nature, some interconnection among them, and more or less of implicit systematic organization. And we need go no further to see that we are now on a higher level of knowledge than before—although it will not do to forget the eminent services which mathematics renders to the sciences of causal and other determination. In the words of Sigwart,

. . . all external events, which we can perceive, are *quanta*, and can be completely and accurately expressed only by quantitative determinations. All change, motion, heating, cooling, etc., in an *A* take place in a certain amount; and in the same way the effect, which consists in the change in *B*, is quantitatively determined. In many instances the *A*'s and *B*'s also, of which the proposition speaks, are capable of quantitative distinctions, even when they are of exactly the same kind; and only when these distinctions are taken into consideration can we say with conceptual accuracy what is to be understood by *A* and *B*, and their changes *a* and *b*. . . . If, indeed, we are to speak accurately, we cannot say that eating stills hunger and drinking thirst, for a mouthful or a sip is no good; nor can we say that arsenic kills or quinine reduces fever, for it depends upon the dose; it is inaccurate, again, to say that common salt is dissolved in water, for it is not true that any quantity of salt is dissolved by any quantity of water.[8]

This, of course, is as far as may be from implying that physics can in any sense be 'reduced' to mathematics; on the contrary, as we have maintained throughout, nothing is more obviously impossible. And this impossibility is clearly recognized in the course of an interesting argument of Peirce's, designed by him to substantiate his thesis of tychism, or spontaneity in nature.[9] Peirce's doctrine might not inaptly be called the epistemological argument for indeterminism in the realm of physical entities, as contrasted with the two arguments briefly discussed in our chapter on "The Physical Sciences," based (1) upon the application of statistical principles to physical phenomena, and (2) upon the detection, by Heisenberg, of a certain waywardness in the behavior of electrons.

Peirce is seeking an explanation of the well-known fact that mathematical computations and physical observations do not precisely agree; in other words, that there is a discrepancy between deductions from the mathematically expressed physical laws and actually observed phenomena. True, 'errors of observation,' and the possibility of more correct formulations of the laws in the course of scientific advance, and the like, account for part of this discrepancy. Peirce contends,

[8] Sigwart, *Logic,* Vol. II, English translation, pp. 346, 347.

[9] Cf. Charles S. Peirce, *Chance, Love and Logic,* especially the essay, "The Doctrine of Necessity Examined."

and contends correctly, however, that no amount of allowance along these lines will completely and in principle resolve the difficulty. Yet the obvious and simple explanation, namely, that causal determination thus shows itself to be more concrete than the purely quantitative, apparently does not occur to him. Instead, he argues that because we cannot, even in principle, make our computations and our observations precisely agree, there must be an element of chance, of spontaneity, making itself evident in physical nature. Spontaneity or chance would account (such is the doctrine) for those deviations from natural law which are otherwise inexplicable.

The natural observation to make on this argument is that at best it affords but flimsy support for Peirce's doctrine. Unless we assumed to begin with that physics may and should be reduced to mathematics without remainder, our real problem would be just the reverse; namely, to account for the exact correspondence of computation and observation, were it *per impossibile* ever to occur.

Of course when we come to the realm of biological phenomena, where, as we have seen, the category of teleology seems to be called for, the state of affairs is somewhat different. And the very fact that Peirce uncritically applies the concept of evolution to physical and social, as well as to organic phenomena, is rather suggestive in this regard.[10] For there is certainly much more plausibility in the view that chance, in the sense

[10] Cf. Chapter VI, above, for criticisms of such an unwarranted extension of the concept of evolution, beyond its proper limits.

of spontaneity, and teleology go hand in hand, than in any other case. If it be true, that, as applied to biological phenomena, teleology represents a relatively 'internal' form of relationship—as contrasted with the quantitative and the causal forms—so that we may speak, though with some hesitancy, of individuality, as manifested, e.g., in the power of self-maintenance, then it would seem that *ipso facto* we must concede a certain degree of spontaneity, of capacity to react in novel ways to various stimuli and at various times, to all living things.

Here again, clearly, we are regarding things from a more inclusive standpoint, but here again we must not forget the contributory value of causal determination, especially emphasized by the rôle assigned to the 'environment.' As Sigwart puts it, in the case of organisms,

> . . . we see combinations of different parts to a whole in the process of formation, without understanding what causes are producing them according to general laws. . . . The maintenance of individuals and of species is a constant, always recurring result; but by what necessity different kinds of matter combine in organic forms, and the particular limbs develop and differentiate, we are unable to explain from the general qualities of matter. Here, therefore, it is natural to explain these phenomena by starting from the whole and its constitution, and inquiring as to the means which will produce this actual result . . . the relation of each part to the unity is understood when we have decided what contribution it yields towards the preservation and maintenance of all the other parts in their combination. . . . [Hence in physiology] the final concept does not contradict the causal treatment, but insists upon it; it is a guiding principle for the discovery of

causal relations; . . . there is no limit to the investigation of causal relations called for by the final concept.[11]

It may appropriately be observed, at this point, that from the biological point of view, the 'environment,' taken by itself, is an abstraction, although from the point of view of physics and chemistry this fact has no significance, since the very term has lost its meaning; as we have said before, there is no environment in a world regarded as causally determined and composed of electrons, protons, and the like.

And just as this purely physical universe acquires a new meaning when viewed in relation to the living organism, so the entire existential order, organic and inorganic, naturally takes on new meaning when regarded in relation to conscious human beings, their individual and social attributes, purposes, and achievements. We have now to do with the nature of mind and experience as a whole, and with the relation of subject to object, rather than merely or solely with organisms or things and their relations to an environment or to other things. The elementary distinctions represented by these differences in terminology are literally tremendous, and there is no excuse for failure to observe them. Obviously any philosophy or system of metaphysics which disregards such distinctions cannot but fail in its essential task—to render every side and aspect of experience intelligible.

We shall return to this interesting point presently. In the meantime we have to continue our explanation

[11] Sigwart, *loc. cit.*, pp. 175, 176. The whole section (78) should be read in this connection.

of the meaning of a philosophical synthesis of the several natural sciences.

Science, we have argued, in various contexts, cannot in any sense *be* philosophy; and neither can philosophy take the place of science. Philosophers may, indeed, amuse themselves and deceive 'the man in the street' by the construction of elaborate systems of cosmology, couched in quasi-scientific technical jargon, so that the resulting picture of the world seems to represent the findings of science itself, whereas in reality hardly anything could be further from the truth. Any such system of cosmology can hardly be more than a fanciful picture, a result of the direction of æsthetic imagination on the intellectual labors of the scientists, rather than a critical evaluation of scientific endeavor.

In this respect, then, a real synthesis of the sciences must acknowledge the relative independence of each science, and in particular must not require of it a contribution to some mythical cosmological system. In so far as it is possible at all the several sciences will themselves show how the world is made, and no amount of imaginative jugglery with quasi-scientific notions—even if the Deity be invoked to complete the picture—will advance the task one whit. While it is platitudinous that the sciences overlap and that each one may assist others, there is also a very real sense in which each is independent of all of the others. Mathematics is invaluable to chemistry, for example, but neither is a substitute for the other, and each has something distinctive to contribute to our knowledge of the existential world.

All of this is doubtless platitudinous. To distinguish the scientific categories—quantity, causality, and so on—in the manner which we have tried to indicate, to show in general how the lower lead on to the higher, while at the same time retaining intact their own significance for knowledge as such, and finally to seek to understand, in the light of these considerations, the place of scientific knowledge in culture as a whole—this is what a genuinely logical synthesis comprises, and such are its invaluable fruits.

The first part of this program we have endeavored to carry out, in a tentative fashion, in the preceding pages. Accordingly it only remains to define, if possible, the place of scientific knowledge in culture as a whole. In other words, we must determine in a general way the significance of natural science relatively to all other forms of human activity. This, of course, may be regarded as too great an undertaking for the close of a small volume, but we may at least hope to render a schematic account sufficient for our present purposes.

Natural science contributes to culture as a whole in several different ways: (1) Pragmatically, i.e., in virtue of the practical applications of scientific knowledge to our general welfare, comfort, and happiness. This is the special function of the applied sciences, so-called, of engineering, medicine, and the like. Hence the partial validity of the assertion of the pragmatist that knowledge exists preëminently in these fields, rather than in science proper.[12] It should not be forgotten, however, in this connection, that science may also be

[12] Cf. Dewey, *Experience and Nature*.

'applied,' indifferently, to the task of destroying values, as in the case of warfare. Hence, every further potential application of knowledge to practice calls for a redefinition of the values to be subserved, and constant watchfulness lest newly acquired powers inspire men to harmful rather than beneficial activities. At best, most mechanical inventions, for example, turn out to be mixed blessings. (2) Theoretically, i.e., in and for its own sake, natural knowledge represents no slight addition to our general culture, to our understanding and appreciation of the world in which we live. Since even instrumentalism—half-heartedly, perhaps—concedes this point, it seems hardly necessary to argue it here. As we have said often enough, the function of science is to reveal the structure and processes of 'nature'—how the world, including man—is made. (3) Lastly, by such a study as we have pursued in the present work, science is made to contribute to a knowledge of ourselves, of our own nature so far as that nature is rational. And this, certainly, is as great a service as any which scientific understanding can render. To realize in and through its typical activities and products the nature of mind as such is perhaps in the long run one of man's major concerns; at all events it is one of the chief concerns of philosophy as we understand it. In other words, it must ever be the function of philosophy to transmute knowledge—scientific, historical, and so forth—into wisdom; which is, after all, but another name for the critical formulation and apprehension of the rational principles immanent in all experience.

And philosophy transmutes scientific knowledge into wisdom precisely by restoring the relation between the subject and the object of knowledge, which relation science of itself is perforce bound to ignore in virtue of its self-imposed task—the determination of the nature of the object in and for itself, ideally conceived of as existing in proud independence of our apprehension of it. This point we referred to a moment ago as one to which we should return, and, we may observe, in now returning to it we are also returning to what is really the underlying theme of this study—as, indeed, we indicated in a preliminary way in chapters I and II above.

But the point we wish particularly to emphasize here is that there is nothing in the relation of physical objects to each other, or in the commerce of organisms with their environment, or in nervous reactions to external stimuli, which at all approaches to this special kind of relationship. Failure to appreciate this fact, simple and obvious as it appears, once it has been pointed out, accounts for the inadequacy and abstractness of contemporary theories of emergent evolution, and at least of those types of idealism and realism which construe the world as all of a piece. The metaphysical evolutionist would, in effect, substitute the relation of the organism to the environment for the relation of subject to object, while both idealists and realists of a certain type set out to construct a synthesis of scientific knowledge by denying or ignoring any such relationship. Thus the timid refusal to 'bifurcate' nature issues in the colorless doctrine that everything 'perceives' everything else; and the so-called empirical assumption that consciousness is just a particular factual relation of essentially the same kind as that of a chair to a table inevitably leads at last to a complete denial of—consciousness.[13] None of these systems can claim the support of science, though each of them pretends to do so, to the manifest embarrassment of each of the others; and much less can any of them even begin to comprehend the philosophical significance of human institutions like the state, or of religion, or of art. To go no further, the very vocabulary necessary for such purposes is lacking to proponents of these inadequate theories. In fact, such aspects of experience and such cultural interests, involving, as they do, not merely the apprehension, but in some sense the constitution, the creation, of the relevant objects—the state, the work of art, and so forth—*ipso facto* entirely transcend the level of these interpretations of experience. In other words, of spiritual *values*, as distinguished—not separated—from physical or quasi-physical existence, these philosophies can have no adequate idea.

Now this emphasis upon the unique and fundamental significance of the subject-object relationship renders desirable a little further indication of what is distinctive about it, what distinguishes it from other empirical relationships, and so, incidentally, an explanation of why it is so often ignored or slurred over.

Let us take for purposes of comparison, the relation-

[13] Just so, to the woman of easy virtue, the words wife and mistress imply little or no distinction of relationship, and hence the institution of the home loses most or all of its meaning for her.

ships (1) of physical objects, (2) of organism and environment, (3) of subject and object.

1. To use a metaphor very common to philosophers—not all of whom seem to realize that it is merely a metaphor—the relation of physical object to physical object is largely 'external.' At the same time, paradoxically enough, the determinate nature of such objects seems to depend mainly on the relations which they bear to other objects, relationships of which the laws of nature are the precise formulations. Perhaps this may be regarded as a corollary to our earlier statements to the effect that the essential individuality of merely physical things is a vanishing one. For these reasons, what one object gains in a physical transaction another loses, so that in the end it appears, as Bergson put it, that *tout est donné*. Changes may take place among the parts of the physical universe, but that realm of being as a whole is static; neither evolution nor development may be predicated of it. There is altogether too much loose talk about the 'dynamic' nature of material entities, where by dynamic we mean something else than merely changing in the sense just indicated.

2. Now all such properties of physical objects follow from the fact that they are, as it were, dominated by spatio-temporal conditions. When we turn to the relationships of the organism and its environment, however, we find a much more complex state of affairs. In the intercourse of living things with their environment, and with each other, spatio-temporal considerations are no doubt of fundamental importance, but there is a

sense, too, in which these considerations are transcended. As we have seen, physical objects are partners on an equal footing in their transactions with the rest of nature and with themselves. So much energy in one form is exchanged for the same amount in another form—throughout the entire domain of the physical sciences quantitative equality must somehow be maintained. And it would seem that this must be so on a merely spatio-temporal level of existence. But in the processes of growth and evolution, involving the consumption of food and so on, the tracing of spatio-temporal and other quantitative relationships is uncertain and of subordinate, though doubtless considerable, importance. And it seems hardly necessary to insist in this place on the patent fact that organisms subsist by transforming and overcoming or subduing their environment to their own purposes. Thus the relationship of one to the other is not, as it is in the case of merely physical things, barely reciprocal. The organism is not food to the merely physical environment, whatever it may be to other organisms. And although one might speak, metaphorically, of food, for example, as an 'object' to an organism, it normally becomes incorporated in the organism in such a way that its *mere* objectivity is completely submerged. In a very real sense the 'object' has become identified with something other than itself, in a fashion totally incomprehensible on the level of the purely physical. Hence we can speak of something more than mere change as taking place, and of something genuinely new as coming into being.

3. Without going further on this subject, the inter-

esting ramifications of which the reader can develop for himself, we may pass at once to a comparison of the subject-object relationship with the foregoing. Confining ourselves to the case of knowledge, which is the only one which directly concerns us here—other equally important cases or aspects being the æsthetic and the practical—we simply note these striking facts as enough sharply to mark off this type of relationship from the two preceding. (*a*) In becoming an object to a subject, in becoming known, that is, the object becomes a part of the world of experience, just as in the domain of life the 'object' becomes the environment to the organism. But to become an environment to an organism entails more or less of alteration in the nature of the object *qua* object (as, e.g., in the case of food), whereas in the case of knowledge the integrity of the object is, by hypothesis, fully preserved. Although we commonly speak of the 'growth' of knowledge, such growth is certainly not at the expense, but rather contributes to the enrichment, of the object. (*b*) Again, when and as known, the object becomes shareable by all 'subjects'; a property of this relationship sufficient of itself to distinguish it from all others. (*c*) Finally, knowledge itself, this 'food of the soul,' becomes its own object, in the peculiar sense briefly defined in Chapter I, above.

Scientific knowledge thus constitues itself, we may say, a revelation not only of nature, but of intelligence, of mind. This is not to say, however, that nature, *qua* nature, is mind-dependent, for it is only by presupposing the independent existence of nature, as we have seen, that we can claim to know nature, and until we know something of nature we can never hope adequately to comprehend the nature of knowledge.

> ". . . speculation," says the poet,
> Speculation "turns not to itself
> Till it hath travelled and is mirrored there
> Where it may see itself."

Hence it is not correct to say, with subjective idealism, that the understanding prescribes laws to nature, or that the existence of anything consists in its being perceived; on the contrary, the laws of nature are nature's own laws, comprehensible to us because our understanding has the power to seek them out, and we perceive things as existing because existence actually appertains to the world of natural phenomena.

But neither is it correct to say, with some forms of realism, or evolutionism, that mind is nature-dependent, except in the peculiar sense specified above. For nature does not apprehend its own laws, and theories of evolution do not themselves evolve. In short, a law of nature ultimately implies *both* an objective order, of which it is a representation, and a principle of intelligibility, of which it is an expression.

From a slightly different angle, but amounting to the same thing in the end, we may say that *in addition to* those properties, characteristics, and relations ascribed by natural science to the existential realm of being as such, philosophy discovers this other property—the property, or capacity, of being known. The least as well as the greatest accomplishments of science would indeed be unintelligible save for this basic presupposition. The other side of this same presupposition, namely, that it is not only the natural desire, but the privilege, of man to know, is also equally implicit in the very fact of scientific knowledge as such. So much is elementary, and tacitly acknowledged, both by the scientist and by the philosopher, with every breath of his intellectual life. And nothing more manifestly emphasizes the fundamental significance of this two-sided relationship than the recent attempts, on the part of certain idealistic and realistic philosophers, to merge the two sides or aspects into an undifferentiated unity. Conversely, the epoch-making contribution to philosophy of Mr. Lovejoy's recent work, *The Revolt Against Dualism,* resides in part in the clear demonstration of the duality of aspects which natural knowledge presupposes. The opponents of 'bifurcation' do well to insist that thought and being are in some sense identical; but the dualist also does well to insist that what is known must be in some sense independent of thought. But what surely cries out for recognition by all hands is, that while natural knowledge implies a unity embracing both the object known and the knower —the object and the subject—no true unity can exist except it be composed of distinct elements, each complementing, fulfilling, the other. Knowledge must not alter the real nature of the object, on pain of ceasing to be knowledge; such is the essential truth driven home with such conclusiveness by Mr. Lovejoy. It needs only to be added that the property of being knowable, while in no wise profaning the sanctity of the object *qua* existential, does, indeed, belong of right to that object, and serves to constitute it an indispensable element in human experience.

In the light of this essential presupposition of scientific knowledge, we can perhaps suggest a satisfactory resolution of a certain long-standing disagreement relative to such knowledge. The so-called English school of neo-Hegelians has been accused, rightly or wrongly, of doing less than scant justice to natural science; of maintaining, in fact, that science distorts or falsifies reality. Certain forms of realism, on the other hand, have been accused of over-emphasizing the findings of science, or the scientific method, even to the extent of equating natural science with philosophy itself. Now from the standpoint of the present work, there is no difficulty in avoiding both of these extreme views, for the province of science has been clearly defined and its findings have been logically evaluated. No arbitrary restrictions from without have been imposed on the search for truth, and neither does there exist the possibility of any undue exaltation of special methods or conceptions. Problems of natural existence are both distinct and inseparable from problems of æsthetic, religious, and logical value—such is the simple principle which has guided our argument throughout, and upon the assumed validity of this principle we are willing, now, in conclusion, to rest our case. In other words, we now know in what sense the world of natural science is independent of our apprehension of it as well as in what sense that world is a part or aspect of a larger world of experience which embraces also many other aspects and interests complementary to and fulfilling the true import of the existential. It follows that the task of philosophy, namely, the theoretical comprehension of human experience in its entirety, involves the differentiation and the integration of these several values in a systematic unity. Towards the accomplishment of this grand undertaking, which every age must inevitably assume for itself, we offer this little book as a modest contribution.

SUGGESTIONS FOR FURTHER STUDY

I

1. Look up the history of the word, 'science.'

2. What criteria of objectivity are suggested by the text? In what would objectivity in a 'social science,' like history, consist?

3. What is meant by the impartiality and disinterestedness of science?

4. Various attempts at a classification of the sciences have been made. (E.g., by Aristotle, Comte, Mill, and Wundt.) Consider the value and significance of such attempts, and try to ascertain the underlying principle in each case.

5. Trace the history of astrology and alchemy, relatively to astronomy and chemistry, respectively.

6. Define for yourself the relation of the logic of science to logic in general.

7. Philosophy is in one sense the most abstract, in another sense the most concrete form of knowledge. Explain this statement. Compare philosophy with mathematics in this respect.

II

1. Consider and develop further, by means of illustrations taken from the history of science, the conception of inference as systematic.

2. Define in relation to each other, the meaning, for natural science, of the terms: fact, law, hypothesis, postulate, principle, theory.

3. What is the distinction between method and technique, rule and principle?

III

1. What is Pythagoreanism?

2. What are some of the logical distinctions between Greek

mathematics and modern mathematics? (Cf., e.g., Latta's *Leibniz,* Introduction.)

3. In what sense is there in all science and not merely in mathematics, an element of 'arbitrariness'?

4. Distinguish carefully between 'continuity' and 'the continuum.'

5. It might be contended that our account of the development of the science of number was mainly of psychological import, rather than a matter of great concern either to the mathematician or to the logician. What reply, if any, could be made to this charge? (Suggestion: treat this as a special case of the wider problem of determining the significance for logic of the history of science in general.)

IV

1. A contrast is often drawn between the 'deductive' and the 'experimental' sciences. Criticize this terminology.

2. Study and illustrate the significance of analogy for scientific inference in general. (Cf. footnote, p. 106.)

3. Consider further the function of the process of construction for mathematics, comparing it with observation and experimentation as they function in the physical sciences.

4. Is there any truth in Kant's conception of the nature of mathematics? Criticize Mill's conception of mathematics.

V

1. Trace the genesis and history (*a*) of the phlogiston theory; (*b*) of the ether theory.

2. In what sense may physics hope to rid itself, gradually, of anthropomorphism, and in what sense not?

3. What logical problem takes the place of the pseudo-epistemological problem of knowledge; better, how does logic, as contrasted with epistemology, formulate the problem of knowledge?

4. Consider the meaning of time for mathematics; for physics; and for chemistry.

5. Show that contingency (objective chance) and human freedom are incommensurable terms.

SUGGESTIONS FOR FURTHER STUDY

VI

1. Trace in more detail the conflict between mechanism, vitalism, and teleology.

2. Study in more detail the development of the idea of evolution. Note particularly its relation to, and its distinction from, the idea of progress in history. (See Bury, *The Idea of Progress.*)

3. Consider further the relation of laws to biological conceptions.

4. Distinguish between atomism and evolutionism as metaphysical theories, and as scientific ones.

VII

1. Draw up a list of metaphors which have been employed in the effort to specify the nature of psychological phenomena and their relation to physical phenomena. Note how many of them depend upon the tacit assumption that the human mind is of the nature of an existential thing.

2. Distinguish carefully between memory in the psychological sense of the word and what is called 'organic' memory.

3. Consider the significance of the fact of meaning for psychology. In what respects does the conception of human nature (*a*) as a physical thing, (*b*) as a biological organism, break down when applied to the explanation of psychological phenomena?

4. Is the distinction between logic, psychology, etc., suggested in the text, entirely satisfactory? If not, how would you amend it?

5. What are some of the important implications of the fact that history has to do with objects in some sense created or constituted by the human mind?

6. Consider the significance of time (*a*) from the biological point of view; (*b*) from the historical point of view. (See *V*, 4.)

VIII

1. Illustrate further the tendency to idealize (i.e., to make a philosophy out of) the various special sciences, and science as a whole.

2. How does cosmology differ from our manner of synthesizing the findings of the several sciences?

3. What is true and what is false in the 'departmental' conception of the sciences, and of knowledge generally?

4. Consider the relation of the problems of value to problems of existence.

5. Reformulate the relation of logic to science, and consider the relation of logic to the other departments of philosophy.

BIBLIOGRAPHY

This bibliography contains only such works as were found especially useful in the preparation of this book. No attempt is made, however, to include either the works of the scientists themselves or a selection from the numerous histories of science. Should he desire to do so, the reader can easily build up his own bibliography in these fields. Immediately following is a short list of books, which, in addition to their own contribution to the subjects with which they deal, will prove especially helpful in this respect.

I

BURTT, E. A.—*The Metaphysical Foundations of Modern Physical Science* (New York, 1925). Contains a bibliography covering the modern period of the physical sciences.

CASSIRER, E.—*Substance and Function and Einstein's Theory of Relativity* (English translation, M. C. and W. C. Swabey. Chicago, 1923). Contains a bibliography on modern physical science.

FRAENKEL, A.—*Einleitung in die Mengenlehre* (3rd ed., Berlin, 1928). Contains a bibliography on the logic of the mathematical sciences.

LEWIS, C. I.—*A Survey of Symbolic Logic* (Berkeley, 1918). See the bibliography for works on the logic of mathematics.

THOMPSON, J. A.—*The System of Animate Nature* (2 vols., New York, 1920). Contains an extensive bibliography of the biological sciences.

Thomson and Geddes.—*Evolution* (New York, 1911). Bibliography of works on the biological sciences.

II

Bergson, Henri.—*Creative Evolution* (English translation by Arthur Mitchell, New York, 1911).

Boas, George.—*A Critical Analysis of the Philosophy of Emile Meyerson* (Baltimore, 1930).

Bosanquet, Bernard.—*Implication and Linear Inference* (London, 1920).

——— *Logic.* Or the Morphology of Knowledge (2 vols., 2nd ed., Oxford, 1911).

Bridgman, P. W.—*The Logic of Modern Physics* (New York, 1927).

Broad, C. D.—*Perception, Physics and Reality* (Cambridge, 1914).

——— *Scientific Thought* (London, 1923).

Brun:chvig, L.—*La causalité physique et l'expérience humaine* (Paris, 1922).

——— *Les étapes de la philosophie mathématique* (2nd ed., Paris, 1922).

Campbell, N. R.—*Physics, The Elements* (Cambridge, 1920).

Conant, L. L.—*The Number Concept.* Its Origin and Development (New York, 1896).

Creighton, J. E.—*Studies in Speculative Philosophy* (H. R. Smart, Ed., New York, 1925).

Croce, Benedetto.—*History: Its Theory and Practice* (English translation by Douglas Ainslee, New York, 1921).

Driesch, Hans.—*The History and Theory of Vitalism* (English translation by C. K. Ogden, London, 1914).

——— *Science and Philosophy of the Organism* (2 vols., New York, 1908).

Duhem, Pierre.—*La théorie physique, son objet et sa structure* (Paris, 1906).

Eddington, A. S.—*The Nature of the Physical World* (New York, 1928).

Einstein, A.—*Relativity.* The Special and General Theory

(English translation by R. W. Lawson, New York, 1920).

HALDANE, J. S.—*Mechanism, Life and Personality* (2nd ed., New York, 1923).

——— *The Sciences and Philosophy* (New York, 1928).

HENDERSON, L. J.—*The Order of Nature* (Cambridge, Mass., 1917).

HOBSON, E. W.—*The Domain of Natural Science* (New York, 1923).

HOERNLÉ, R. F. A.—*Matter, Life, Mind and God* (London, 1923).

HÖLDER, Otto.—*Die mathematische Methode* (Berlin, 1924).

JEVONS, W. S.—*The Principles of Science* (2nd ed., London, 1892).

JOSEPH, H. W. B.—*An Introduction to Logic* (2nd ed., Oxford, 1916).

KEYNES, J. M.—*Treatise on Probability* (London, 1921).

LALANDE, A.—*Les théories de l'induction et de l'expérimentation* (Paris, 1929).

——— *Les illusions évolutionnistes* (Paris, 1930).

LANGE, F. A.—*History of Materialism* (English translation by E. C. Thomas, 3rd ed., New York, 1925).

LASSWITZ, K.—*Geschichte der Atomistik vom Mittelalter bis Newton* (Hamburg, 1890).

MACH, E.—*Popular Scientific Lectures* (English translation by Thomas J. McCormack, Chicago, 1895).

——— *The Science of Mechanics* (English translation by Thomas J. McCormack, 4th ed., Chicago, 1919).

MEYERSON, E.—*La déduction rélativiste* (Paris, 1925).

——— *De l'explication dans les sciences* (2 vols., Paris, 1921).

——— *Identity and Reality* (English translation by K. Loewenberg, New York, 1930).

NATORP, Paul.—*Die logischen Grundlagen der exakten Wissenschaften* (Berlin, 1910).

PEARSON, Karl.—*The Grammar of Science* (3rd ed., London, 1911).

PEIRCE, C. S.—*Chance, Love and Logic* (New York, 1923).

PLANCK, Max.—*A Survey of Physics* (New York, 1913).

——— *Acht Vorlesungen ueber theoretische Physik* (Leipzig, 1911).

POINCARÉ, Henri.—*The Foundations of Science* (English translation by G. B. Halstead, New York, 1913).

RUSSELL, B.—*The Analysis of Matter* (New York, 1927).

——— *An Introduction to Mathematical Philosophy* (New York, 1919).

SIGWART, Christoph.—*Logic* (English translation by Helen Dendy, 2 vols., 2nd ed., New York, 1895).

SMART, H. R.—*The Philosophical Presuppositions of Mathematical Logic* (Cornell Studies in Philosophy, Ithaca, 1925).

SPAIER, A.—*La pensée et la quantité* (Paris, 1927).

WEYL, Hermann.—*Space, Time, Matter* (English translation by H. L. Brose, London, 1922).

WHEWELL, W.—*History of the Inductive Sciences from the Earliest to the Present Time* (3 vols., London, 1847).

WHITEHEAD, A. N.—*Introduction to Mathematics* (London, 1911).

——— *Science and the Modern World* (New York, 1925).

WOLF, A.—*Essentials of Scientific Method* (New York, 1925).

INDEX

INDEX

INDEX

(1)